Practical Problems in Mathematics

FOR
Automotive Technicians

Practical Problems in Mathematics

FOR
Automotive Technicians

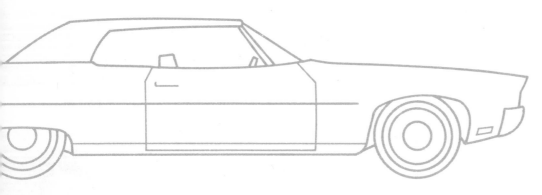

$$A = \frac{3.1416\, d^2}{4}$$

$$HP = \frac{D^2 N}{2.5}$$

DELMAR PUBLISHERS
COPYRIGHT © 1972
BY LITTON EDUCATIONAL PUBLISHING, INC.

LIBRARY OF CONGRESS CATALOG CARD NUMBER: 78 – 174884

PRINTED IN THE UNITED STATES OF AMERICA
PUBLISHED SIMULTANEOUSLY IN CANADA BY
DELMAR PUBLISHERS, A DIVISION OF
VAN NOSTRAND REINHOLD, LTD.

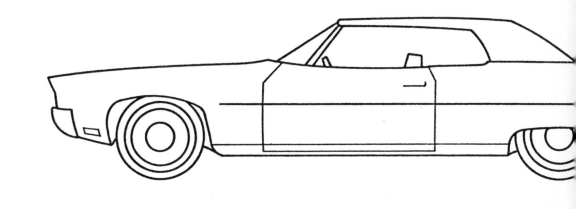

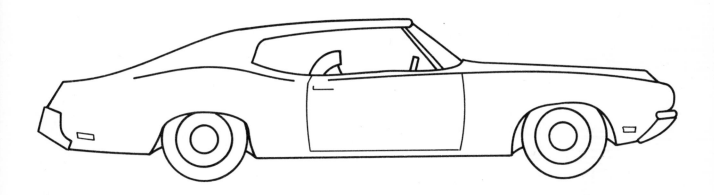

$$I = \frac{E}{R}$$

$$PD = 7854^2 LN$$

Boyce H. Dwiggins, Assistant Supervisor
Vocational Technical Education
School Board of Broward County
Fort Lauderdale, Florida

DELMAR PUBLISHERS • MOUNTAINVIEW AVENUE • ALBANY, NEW YORK 12205

A DIVISION OF LITTON EDUCATIONAL PUBLISHING, INC.

CONTENTS

SECTION 1   WHOLE NUMBERS

SECTION 2   FRACTIONS

SECTION 3   DECIMALS

SECTION 4   PERCENTAGE

SECTION 5 MEASUREMENT

SECTION 6 RATIO AND PROPORTION

SECTION 7 POWERS AND ROOTS

SECTION 8 FORMULAS

SECTION 9 GRAPHS

SECTION 10 INVOICES

Unit 1 ADDITION OF WHOLE NUMBERS

BASIC PRINCIPLES OF ADDITION

- Study unit 1 in *Basic Mathematics Simplified* for the principles of addition as applied to whole numbers.
- Apply the principles of addition to the automotive field by solving the Review Problems which follow.

REVIEW PROBLEMS

1. In wiring a trailer, the following lengths of wire are used: 6 feet, 3 feet, 8 feet, and 10 feet. What is the total length of wire used? _____

2. In repairing a car, the following number of new bolts is necessary: 5 head bolts, 8 oil pan bolts, 3 fender bolts, and 6 differential cover bolts. How many bolts are used in all? _____

3. In taking inventory, the following spark plugs are checked: 100 of the 14 millimeter (mm) plugs, 72 of the 18 mm plugs and 15 of the 10 mm plugs. What is the total number of plugs on inventory? _____

4. A mechanic needs the following lengths of 3/8-inch copper tubing: one piece 15 inches, one piece 8 inches, one piece 10 inches, one piece 11 inches, one piece 16 inches, one piece 9 inches, and two pieces 12 inches. What total length of tubing is required for the job? _____

5. On five different trips an automobile is driven 33 miles, 27 miles, 19 miles, 42 miles, and 24 miles. What is the total mileage driven? _____

6. What is the total gasoline consumption for one week if a driver uses 10 gallons, 6 gallons, 2 gallons, 9 gallons, 8 gallons, 3 gallons, and 12 gallons? _____

7. A mechanic removes 27 nuts from the cylinder head, 34 nuts from the oil pan and 9 nuts from the flywheel housing. What is the total number of nuts removed? _____

8. Headlights draw 10 amperes of current; ignition coil, 4 amperes; taillight, 2 amperes; car heater, 8 amperes. What is the total amperage drawn from the battery? _____

9. An automotive stock clerk has 53 of the 1/2-inch castellated nuts in stock. He orders 864 additional nuts. How many does he now have in stock? _____

10. A driver drives his car 129 miles to one city, 134 miles to another, and 219 miles home. What is the total mileage driven? _____

Unit 2   SUBTRACTION OF WHOLE NUMBERS

BASIC PRINCIPLES OF SUBTRACTION

- Study unit 2 in *Basic Mathematics Simplified* for the principles of subtraction as applied to whole numbers.

- Apply the principles of subtraction to the automotive field by solving the Review Problems which follow.

REVIEW PROBLEMS

1. A car measures 16 feet in length; the garage is 21 feet long inside. How much clearance is there when the car is parked in the garage?   _____

2. If 39 quarts of oil are removed from a stock of 350 quarts, how many quarts are left in stock?   _____

3. Driver number one drives his car 169 miles while driver number two drives his car 272 miles. How much farther does number two drive than number one?   _____

4. An inventory sheet shows 365 pounds of body lead. If 24 pounds are used on one job and 17 pounds on a second job, how many pounds are left?   _____

5. A stock clerk fills orders for 6, 8, 4, 16, 12, and 24 spark plugs from a stock of 153 plugs. How many plugs are left in stock after filling the orders?   _____

6. A 250-foot coil of ignition wire is taken out of stock. The following lengths are cut off: 2 feet, 3 feet, 1 foot, 3 feet, 2 feet. How much wire is left in the coil?   _____

7. In a period of a month, one driver uses 93 gallons of gasoline while another driver uses 54 gallons. How much more gasoline does the first driver use than the second?   _____

8. If 47 washers are taken from a box containing 126 washers, how many washers are left?   _____

9. A bill for repairs is $247; a discount of $24 is given. How much does the customer pay for his repairs?   _____

10. An automobile is driven 31,103 miles, of which 11, 392 miles are on company business. How many miles are driven on personal business?   _____

Unit 3   MULTIPLICATION OF WHOLE NUMBERS

BASIC PRINCIPLES OF MULTIPLICATION

- Study unit 3 in *Basic Mathematics Simplified* for the principles of multiplication as applied to whole numbers.

- Apply the principles of multiplication to the automotive field by solving the Review Problems which follow.

REVIEW PROBLEMS

1. How far does a car travel in 6 hours if the speed is held constant at 34 miles an hour?   _____

2. A car consumes gasoline at the rate of 1 gallon to every 17 miles. How many miles does the car travel on 199 gallons of gasoline?   _____

3. If a car moves 9 feet in one revolution of a wheel, how many feet does it move in 427 revolutions of the wheel?   _____

4. How many miles does a car driven 45 miles an hour cover in 7 hours?   _____

5. A gasoline tank on a car holds 19 gallons. How far does the car travel with one tank of gasoline if it averages 16 miles to a gallon?   _____

6. A car travels at the rate of 52 miles an hour for 5 hours on Monday, 43 miles an hour for 6 hours on Tuesday, 47 miles an hour for 9 hours on Wednesday. What is the total mileage driven?   _____

7. A coil from an automobile has 57 layers of wire wound on it with 346 turns per layer. How many turns of wire are in the coil?   _____

8. There are 9 trim clips used to hold the upholstered door panel on one door. How many trim clips are needed to hold the panels on all four doors of 14 cars?   _____

9. A car has 31 of the 2-candlepower bulbs, 2 of the 21-candlepower bulbs, 4 of the 6-candlepower bulbs, and 3 of the 15-candlepower bulbs. What is the total candlepower of the bulbs?   _____

10. A body shop man estimates that an average of 18 pop rivets is used on each body repair job. If an average of 18 jobs is done per month, how many pop rivets must be ordered for 2 months work?   _____

Unit 4   DIVISION OF WHOLE NUMBERS

BASIC PRINCIPLES OF DIVISION

- Study unit 4 in *Basic Mathematics Simplified* for the principles of division as applied to whole numbers.

- Apply the principles of division to the automotive field by solving the Review Problems which follow.

REVIEW PROBLEMS

1. Jim travels 7021 miles which is 7 times as far as John travels. How far does John travel?   _____

2. A garage buys 52 feet of heater hose. How many cars can be repaired if each car uses 13 feet of hose?   _____

3. If a mechanic is paid $14.00 per day, how many days does he have to work to earn $168.00?   _____

4. A stock clerk has 256 spark plugs in stock; there are 8 plugs in a box. How many boxes of plugs does he have in stock?   _____

5. A man drives his car 384 miles. If his car averages 16 miles per gallon, how many gallons of gasoline are used?   _____

6. On a trip, a car uses 21 gallons of gasoline while traveling 378 miles. How many miles per gallon does the car average?   _____

7. A car weighs 3280 pounds. What is the average weight per wheel?   _____

8. In one revolution of a wheel the car moves 8 feet. How many revolutions are required to move the car 1 mile?   _____

9. Two automobile mechanics working together work a total of 240 hours on a job. If they work 8 hours a day, 5 days a week, how many weeks does the job take?   _____

10. If the valves on a 6-cylinder engine are reconditioned in 180 minutes, how much time does it take to recondition each valve?   _____

11. A garage owner uses 38 gallons of motor oil to make oil changes in 25 automobiles. How many full quarts (on the average) does each require?   _____

12. A driver travels 941 miles in three days. If he travels 5 hours on Monday, 6 hours on Tuesday, and 9 hours on Wednesday, what is his average speed for the trip?   _____

Unit 5 SCALE READING

BASIC PRINCIPLES OF SCALE READING

- Study unit 6 in *Basic Mathematics Simplified* for the principles of scale reading as applied to fractions.

- Apply the principles of scale reading to the automotive field by solving the Review Problems which follow.

REVIEW PROBLEMS

1. On the upper part of the scale each division equals 1/16 inch, or there are 16 divisions to the inch. How many 1/16 inch are there in 4 inches?   _____

2. There are 8/8 in an inch. How many 1/8 inch are there in the diameter of a 3-inch piston?   _____

3. How many 1/16 inch are there in a 5/8-inch shackle bolt?   _____

4. How many 1/16 inch are there in a 3/4-inch kingpin?   _____

5. How many 1/16 are there in 1/4 inch?   _____

6. How many 1/16 are there in 7/8 inch?   _____

7. How many 1/8 are there in 3/4 inch?   _____

8. What is the size of a piece 1/8 inch larger than 1/4 inch?   _____

9. What is the size of a piece 1/16 inch larger than 1/2 inch?   _____

10. What is the size of a piece 1/4 inch larger than 5/8 inch?   _____

11. What is the size of a piece 1/16 inch larger than 2 3/8 inches?   _____

Give the scale readings indicated by numbers 12 through 20. Record each dimension in the space provided.

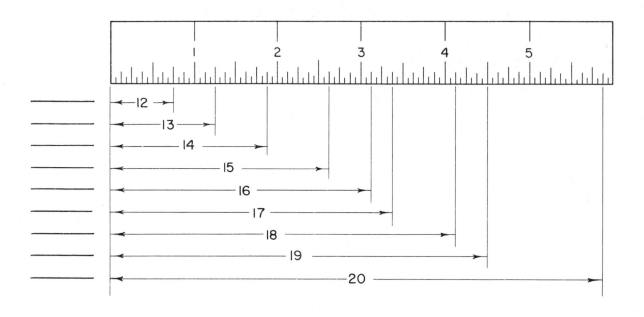

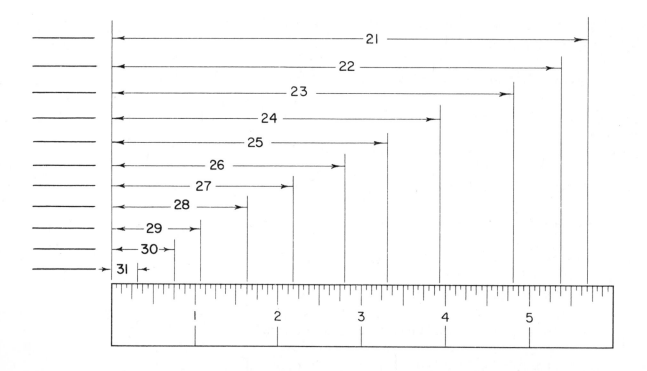

Using your scale, measure and give the length in the following problems: (Note: measure to nearest 1/32 inch.)

32. |————————| 38. |————————————|

33. |————————————| 39. |———————————————|

34. |—————————————| 40. |——————————————|

35. |———————| 41. |—————————————————|

36. |—————————| 42. |———————————————|

37. |——————————————| 43. |—————————|

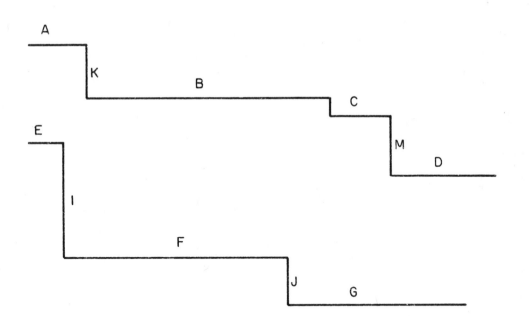

44. Measure and give the total length of A + B + C + D.   _____

45. Measure and give the total length of E + F + G.   _____

46. Measure and give the total length of I + J.   _____

47. Measure and give the total length of K + L + M.   _____

Unit 6 ADDITION OF FRACTIONS

BASIC PRINCIPLES OF ADDITION

- Study unit 7 in *Basic Mathematics Simplified* for the principles of addition as applied to fractions.

- Apply the principles of addition to the automotive field by solving the Review Problems which follow.

REVIEW PROBLEMS

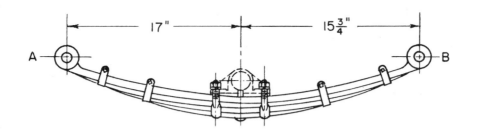

1. What is the length of the spring from the center of eye A to the center of eye B?   _____

2. If the 17-inch dimension is changed to 16 3/4 inches, what is the length of the spring?   _____

3. If the measurements are given as 17 5/8 inches and 14 7/8 inches, what is the spring length?   _____

4. If the measurements are given as 18 3/4 inches and 15 3/8 inches, what is the spring length?   _____

5. A mechanic works 2 1/4 hours on one car, 1 1/2 hours on another car, and 5 3/4 hours on a third car. What is the total amount of time worked?   _____

6. A garage owner has four pieces of vacuum hose of the following lengths: 9 3/4 feet, 10 1/4 feet, 49 1/2 feet, and 12 feet. How many feet of vacuum hose does he have in stock?   _____

7. A truck hauls in one day three loads of stone of the following weights: 3 1/4 tons, 4 1/8 tons, and 3 1/2 tons. What is the total tonnage carried during that day?   _____

8. The chassis of a truck is 14 3/4 feet long. Its body projects at the rear 4 1/2 feet beyond the end of the frame. If there is 3 3/4 feet clearance space at each end of the truck when it is in the garage, what is the inside length of the garage in feet?   _____

9. In the drawing, what is the thickness of the crossmember and frame at the point where the hole is drilled?

    _____

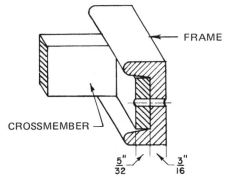

FRAME

CROSSMEMBER

$\frac{5"}{32}$ $\frac{3"}{16}$

10. If the frame is 7/16 inch thick, what is the combined thickness of both members?

    _____

11. In a car with a crossmember 1/8 inch thick and a frame 3/32 inch thick, how much stock is drilled to pierce both members?

    _____

12. A truck frame is 3/16 inch thick. The crossmember is 13/64 inch thick. How much stock is drilled to pierce both members?

    _____

13. In the illustration, what is the under-the-head length of bolt used?

    _____

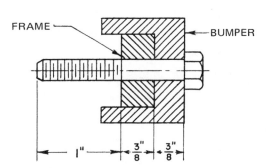

FRAME

BUMPER

$1"$ $\frac{3"}{8}$ $\frac{3"}{8}$

14. If the same bumper is used but there is only 13/16 inch projecting beyond the frame, what length bolt is necessary?

    _____

15. What length bolt (under-the-head) is necessary if the bumper is 7/16 inch thick, the frame is 1/4 inch and there is 5/8 inch projecting?

    _____

16. A frame member is 3/16 inch thick. The gusset plate attaching the crossmember to the side member of the frame is 9/64 inch thick. These pieces are drilled for a 3/8-inch diameter rivet. Allowing 9/64 inch for heading over the end, how long is the rivet under the head?

    _____

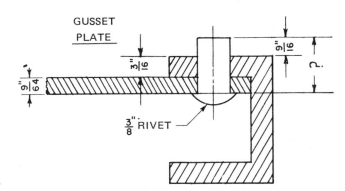

GUSSET PLATE

$\frac{9"}{16}$

$\frac{3"}{16}$

?

$\frac{9"}{64}$

$\frac{3"}{8}$ RIVET

17. If a 1/4-inch diameter rivet is used with the same size gusset plate and frame member and 3/8 inch is allowed for heading over the end, what is the length of rivet under the head?

    _____

18. With a 5/32-inch gusset plate, a 11/64-inch frame member, and a 1/4-inch allowance for heading over, what is the length of rivet under the head?

    _____

MAIN BEARING JOURNALS

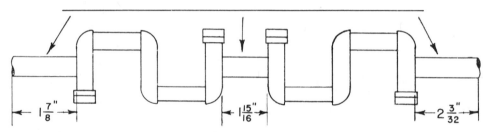

19. What is the total length of main bearing journals in this crankshaft? _____

20. With journal lengths of 1 3/4 inches, 1 29/32 inches, and 1 57/64 inches, what is the total length of main bearing journals? _____

21. An interior refinishing job calls for the following simulated wood panel trim: dash, 2 pieces 8 3/4 inches x 2 1/4 inches x 3/16 inch; 2 pieces 7 1/2 inches x 2 1/4 inches x 3/16 inch; doors, 2 pieces 8 3/4 inches x 2 1/4 inches x 3/16 inch; 2 pieces 7 1/2 inches x 2 1/4 inches x 3/16 inch. What total length of trim is required for the job? _____

22. A door panel trim job on an automobile requires the following pieces of simulated wood on each door: one piece 15 1/2 inches x 2 inches x 3/16 inch, one piece 8 9/32 inches x 2 inches x 3/16 inch. What is the total length of trim required on each door? _____

23. A repairman uses lengths of copper tubing for oil lines as follows: 12 7/32 inches, 14 9/64 inches, 9 7/16 inches, 4 inches, 7 1/8 inches, and 6 7/8 inches. What is the total length of tubing used? _____

HOSE

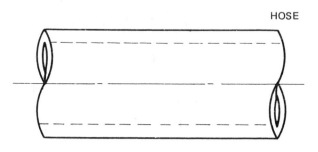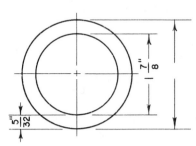

24. A piece of hose, 1 7/8 inches inside diameter, has a wall thickness of 5/32 inch. What is the outside diameter? _____

25. Find the outside diameter of a piece of hose with a 1 3/4-inch inside diameter and a wall thickness of 7/32 inch. _____

26. What is the outside diameter of a piece of copper tubing, inside diameter 5/16 inch, wall thickness 3/32 inch? _____

27. What is the outside diameter of a pipe with a 3/16-inch wall and a 1 1/2-inch inside diameter? _____

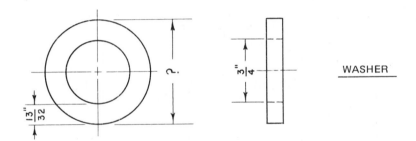

WASHER

28. What is the outside diameter of a washer with a 3/4-inch hole and 13/32 inch between the hole and outside edge? _____

29. If the washer has a 15/16-inch hole and 11/32 inch between the hole and outside on each side, what is its outside diameter? _____

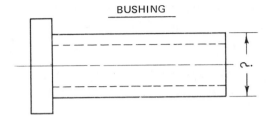

BUSHING

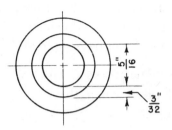

30. A shaft 5/16 inch in diameter is to run in a bronze bushing with a wall thickness of 3/32 inch. What size hole is drilled for the bushing? _____

31. If the shaft in question 30 is 1/2 inch in diameter and the bronze bushing is 5/32 inch thick, what size hole is drilled for the bushing? _____

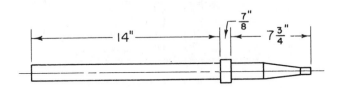

32. What is the overall length of the axle shaft shown above? _____

33. If the 14-inch dimension is changed to 16 9/16 inches, what is the overall length? _____

34. How long is the axle shaft with the following dimensions: 21 inches, 15/16 inch, 7 7/8 inches? _____

35. How long is the axle shaft with the following dimensions: 17 13/16 inches, 9/32 inch, 6 1/2 inches? _____

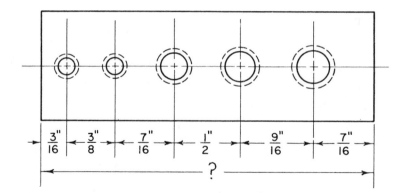

36. What length piece is used to make this drill and top block?   _____

37. A mechanic needs the following lengths of 3/8-inch copper tubing: 14 1/2 inches, 7 3/8 inches, 11 15/16 inches and 16 15/32 inches. How much does he need in all?   _____

38. A mechanic works 2 1/4 hours on one car, 5 1/2 hours on another, and 3 hours on a third. How many hours does he spend on the three cars?   _____

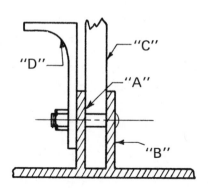

39. What length bolts are purchased to hold the illustrated assembly together if "A" and "B" are 7/32 inch thick, "C" is 1 1/2 inches thick, and "D" is 5/32 inch thick; allowance is made for a nut 7/16 inch thick and 3/16 inch is allowed for heading the end of the bolt over after the nut is put on.   _____

40. How long are the bolts if "A" and "B" are 3/8 inch thick, "C" is 1 3/16 inches thick, "D" is 3/16 inch thick, the nut is 3/8 inch thick, and allowance of 5/32 inch is made for heading over the end of the bolt?   _____

41. In rewiring the ignition system of a car, a repairman uses the following lengths of high tension wire: 18 3/16 inches, 21 7/8 inches, 18 inches, 19 3/8 inches, 24 7/32 inches. What is the total length of wire used?   _____

Unit 7   SUBTRACTION OF FRACTIONS

BASIC PRINCIPLES OF SUBTRACTION

- Study unit 8 in *Basic Mathematics Simplified* for the principles of subtraction as applied to fractions.

- Apply the principles of subtraction to the automotive field by solving the Review Problems which follow.

REVIEW PROBLEMS

1. If the outside diameter of a hose is 2 1/4 inches and the wall is 13/32-inch thick, how large is the inside diameter? _____

2. A piece of 1/4-inch copper tubing measures 9/16 inch outside. What is the difference between the inside and outside diameter? _____

3. If the outside diameter of a hose is 1 11/16 inches and the wall is 3/16 inch thick, what is the size of the inside diameter? _____

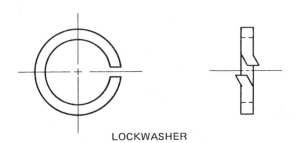

LOCKWASHER

4. The lockwasher used on a 3/8-inch bolt measures 25/64 inch inside diameter, and 5/8 inch, outside diameter. What is the difference between the inside and outside diameters? _____

5. What is the clearance between the lockwasher in problem 4 and the 3/8-inch diameter bolt? _____

6. If the lockwasher used on a 1/2-inch bolt measures 27/32 inch outside diameter and the ring is 5/32 inch in width, what is the inside diameter? _____

7. If the lockwasher used on a 3/4-inch bolt measures 25/32 inch, inside diameter, and the ring is 3/16 inch in width, what is the outside diameter? _____

8. What is the clearance between a 5/8-inch bolt and a lockwasher which measures 1 3/64 inches outside diameter and has a ring width of 3/16 inch? _____

9. If a strip of copper 3/32 inch thick is wrapped around a shaft 1 3/16 inches in diameter, what is the new diameter? _____

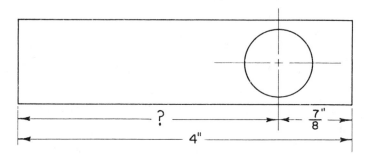

10. What is the missing dimension in the drawing above?

11. If the length of stock is 5 1/2 inches instead of 4 inches, what is the missing dimension?

12. If a piece of stock 6 3/4 inches long has a hole drilled with its center 2 5/16 inches from one end, how far is it from the center of the hole to the other end of the stock?

13. What is the length of the short end on an automobile leaf spring if the complete spring is 32 inches long and the long end is 18 3/8 inches?

14. A radiator contains 14 1/2 quarts of water. How much water remains in the radiator after 3 1/2 quarts are drawn out?

15. An automobile driver has planned to drive 325 1/4 miles in a day. By the middle of the afternoon, he has driven 267 3/4 miles. How many miles remain to be driven?

16. A drum of grease complete with container weighs 420 1/2 pounds. What does the grease weigh if the container weighs 46 1/4 pounds?

17. A mechanic needs an axle shaft key 1/4 inch square. The only available piece of key stock measures 1/4 inch x 3/8 inch. What thickness of stock has to be removed to bring it to proper size?

18. The front wheels of a car are not parallel but set to toe-in; that is, the front edges are closer together than the back. The toe-in measurement of a certain car is 3/8 inch. The specifications call for a toe-in of 3/16 inch. Is the toe-in to be increased or decreased? How much?

19. Replacing bolts in a frame, a mechanic finds he needs six bolts 5/16 inch in diameter and 5/8 inch long. The only size available is 5/16 inch by 1 1/4 inches long. How much does he cut off each bolt?

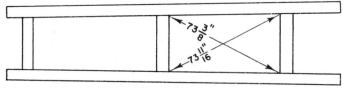

20. A mechanic, in checking a frame for alignment finds that one diagonal measures 73 11/16 inches and the other measures 7 3/8 inches. What is the difference in the measurements taken? (See sketch above.)

21. If the measurements are 87 1/16 inches and 86 9/32 inches, what is the difference? _____

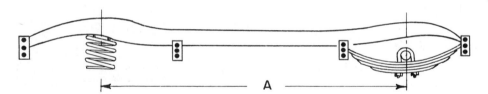

A

22. The front axle of a car is to be aligned with the rear axle; measurement A on one side of the car is 9 feet 3 3/4 inches and on the other side of the car it is 9 feet 4 5/16 inches. How much does one side need to be shifted to bring the axles into alignment? _____

23. If measurement A on one side of the car is 108 7/32 inches and on the other side is 109 3/16 inches, how much out of alignment are the two axles? _____

24. The long end of a spring is 21 7/16 inches. How long is the short end of the spring if the overall length is 33 1/2 inches? _____

25. Two splice plates are cut from a piece of sheet steel that has an overall length of 15 3/4 inches. The plates are 6 7/8 inches and 7 5/16 inches long. How much material is left if 1/16 inch is allowed for each saw cut? _____

26. A repairman works 1 1/4 hours on one car, 3 3/4 hours on another car, and 1 1/4 hours on a third car. How much time remains for another job in an 8-hour working day? _____

27. What is the missing dimension of the clevis pin? _____

28. If the 1/4-inch dimension is changed to 3/8 inch, what is the missing dimension now? _____

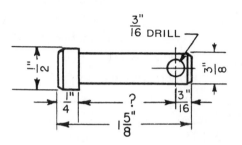

29. If total length is changed to 1 3/4 inches and the 1/4-inch dimension is used, what is the missing dimension? _____

30. What is the difference in size between the two ends of the clevis pin? _____

31. How far is the center of the hole from the top (including the head) of the pin? _____

32. In the accompanying sketch, what is the depth of the drilled hole?

    _____

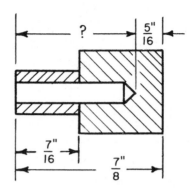

33. If the hole has been drilled 7/16 inch deep, how much deeper must it be drilled?

    _____

34. If it is necessary to keep the hole 1/2 inch from the bottom, to what depth should the hole be drilled?

    _____

35. A truck has an overall length of 15 3/4 feet. How much clearance space is left in a garage 25 feet long inside, if a bench 2 1/4 feet wide is placed in front of the truck?

    _____

36. The top of the cab of a truck is 8 1/2 feet from the ground. The top of the body is 3 3/4 feet above the cab. What clearance is there in going under a bridge that has a clearance of 13 3/4 feet?

    _____

37. Find the missing dimension in the wheel hub drawing.   A = 1/16 inch, B = 9/16 inch, C = 31/32 inch, D = 5/16 inch, E = 4 5/32 inches.

    _____

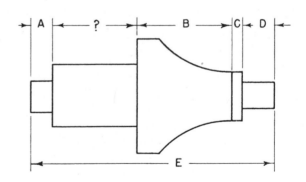

38. A garage owner has a piece of radiator hose that is 69 inches long. He cuts from it short pieces as follows: 5 1/8 inches, 6 7/16 inches, 9 16/32 inches, 4 inches, 5 7/8 inches, and 15 3/8 inches. How many inches remain?

    _____

39. The following amounts are taken from a 5-gallon can of oil: 3/4 gallon, 1 3/4 gallons, 1 1/2 gallons, and 1/8 gallon. How many gallons remain?

    _____

40. A gasoline tank contains 18 1/2 gallons of gasoline. The owner uses 7 3/4 gallons on one trip and 2 1/3 gallons on another. How many gallons of gasoline remain in the tank?

    _____

41. Find the measurement of A in the sketch shown. _____

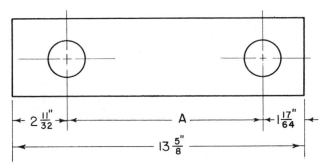

42. A workman is allowed 14 1/2 hours to complete a job. He works on the job five different times as follows: 1/2 hour, 1 1/4 hours, 7 3/4 hours, 1 1/4 hours, and 3/4 hour. How much remains to complete the job? _____

43. A garageman uses a 7 1/2 horsepower electric motor to run his air pump _____ and machine shop. If his machine shop requires 4 1/2 horsepower and the air pump requires 3/4 horsepower, what amount of power is still available for other uses?

The following problems are to be done mentally. When you have completed this page, your instructor will test your ability to add and subtract dimensions without the use of paper and pencil.

Note: Dimensions may be added by sliding the thumb along the scale and observing the final reading. Use the scale where necessary in these problems.

Note: The symbol ('') is used to represent inch or inches.

Addition		Subtraction	
44. 3/8'' + 5/8''	_____	64. 1'' – 3/8''	_____
45. 1/4'' + 1/8''	_____	65. 3/4'' – 1/8''	_____
46. 1/2'' + 3/8''	_____	66. 1/2'' – 3/16''	_____
47. 5/16'' + 7/16''	_____	67. 1 1/4'' – 1/16''	_____
48. 3/16'' + 1/4''	_____	68. 1 1/2'' – 5/16''	_____
49. 7/8'' + 1/16''	_____	69. 2 3/4'' – 5/8''	_____
50. 9/16'' + 1/4''	_____	70. 3 5/8'' – 7/16''	_____
51. 3/4'' + 3/16''	_____	71. 1 1/4'' – 5/8''	_____
52. 11/16'' + 1/8''	_____	72. 2 1/2'' – 11/16''	_____
53. 1/8'' + 3/16''	_____	73. 3 7/8'' – 15/16''	_____
54. 3/8'' + 1 1/4''	_____	74. 1 3/4'' + 5/8'' – 3/8''	_____
55. 7/16'' + 1 3/4''	_____	75. 1 1/2'' + 1'' – 5/16''	_____
56. 1 1/2'' + 3/16''	_____	76. 2'' – 7/16'' + 3/8''	_____
57. 9/16'' + 1 5/8'' + 1/4''	_____	77. 3 5/8'' + 7/8'' – 1/4''	_____
58. 2 3/8'' + 1 5/16'' + 3/4''	_____	78. 2 1/4'' – 3/4'' + 5/16''	_____
59. 3 1/8'' + 1/2'' + 7/16''	_____	79. 13/16'' – 3/8'' + 1 5/8''	_____
60. 1 11/16'' + 5/8'' + 2''	_____	80. 11/16'' + 7/16'' – 1/2''	_____
61. 15/16'' + 1 1/4'' + 1/8''	_____	81. 2 7/8'' – 1 5/16'' + 1/4''	_____
62. 5/8'' + 13/16'' + 2 1/4''	_____	82. 3'' + 2 1/4'' – 7/8''	_____
63. 13/16'' + 3 5/8'' + 1/2''	_____	83. 2 7/16'' + 3/8'' – 15/16''	_____

Unit 8 MULTIPLICATION OF FRACTIONS

BASIC PRINCIPLES OF MULTIPLICATION

- Study unit 9 in *Basic Mathematics Simplified* for the principles of multiplication as applied to fractions.

- Apply the principles of multiplication to the automotive field by solving the Review Problems which follow.

REVIEW PROBLEMS

1. How many pounds of grease are there in a barrel which holds approximately 54 gallons? (Use 7 7/8 pounds per gallon.)

2. What is the weight of the grease in a 54-gallon drum if there were approximately 7 3/4 pounds per gallon?

3. A repairman cuts 12 pieces of copper tubing from a coil. Each piece is 37 7/16 inches long. What is the total length used?

4. A mechanic cuts 5 bushings from a piece of stock. Each bushing is 7/8 inch long. What is the total length used, not allowing for saw cuts?

5. If one piston weighs 3/4 of a pound, what do 8 pistons weigh?

6. A gasoline tank holds 15 gallons. How many miles is it possible to travel on one tank of gasoline at 14 6/10 miles per gallon?

7. If a car averages 18 1/2 miles to a gallon of gasoline, how many miles can be traveled on 37 gallons?

8. If a man drives a car an average of 275 1/2 miles a day, how far does he drive in 4 3/4 days?

9. If an auto travels a mile in 49 seconds, how long does it take to travel 5/8 of a mile at the same rate?

10. An auto averages 45 5/10 miles per hour on a trip. How far does it go in 7 3/4 hours?

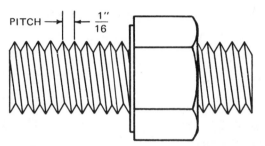

Note: On a 16 NF thread the nut advances 1/16 inch per revolution, on a 28 NF it advances 1/28 inch, etc.

11. How far will a nut advance with 14 turns on a 1/4-inch — 28 NF (National Fine Thread) bolt?

12. How far will a nut advance with 15 turns on a 1/4-inch — 20 NC (National Coarse Thread) bolt?   _____

13. How far will a nut advance with 6 turns on a 3/4-inch — 16 NF bolt?   _____

A certain car (4-door) requires rubber door gasket material as follows:

Each rear door   —   34 7/8 inches

Each front door   —   19 3/4 inches

14. How much gasket material is required for two rear doors?   _____

15. How much gasket material is required for two front doors?   _____

16. How much gasket material is required for all four doors?   _____

17. A certain car requires 22 3/16 inches of 13/32-inch air conditioning hose. How many feet and inches of hose are required for four cars?   _____

18. How many feet of power steering return hose is needed to replace the hose on eight units if each unit requires 9 3/4 inches?   _____

19. The specifications of a certain car call for 4 pieces of rubber door gasket each 14 1/4 inches long and 4 pieces each 15 1/2 inches long. What is the total length needed?   _____

20. A certain car requires 25 1/2 inches of 1/2-inch air conditioning hose. How many feet are necessary to replace the hose in four cars?   _____

21. Five lengths of radiator hose, each 2 7/8 inches long, are cut from a piece of hose 24 1/2 inches long. How much hose is left in the piece?   _____

22. A channel iron crossmember weighs 2 1/2 pounds per foot. What is the weight of five equal crossmembers each 2 1/2 feet long?   _____

23. Tubular steel crossmembers weigh 3 1/8 pounds per foot of length. What is the weight of two of these members, one 2 feet long and one 2 1/2 feet long?   _____

24. The cooling system of a certain Chevrolet has a capacity of 3 1/2 gallons. If a solution which is 5/8 alcohol offers winter protection against freezing, how many quarts of alcohol are used?   _____

25. The capacity of a cooling system is 3 3/4 gallons. The owner wants protection against freezing to a temperature of –10°F. If 4 parts alcohol and 3 parts water give this protection, how many quarts of alcohol are used?   _____

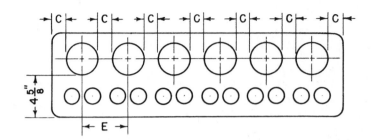

26. Find the total length of the cylinder block surface, if the cylinders are 3 1/16 inches in diameter and the distance C is 5/8 inch. _____

27. What is the center to-center distance E? _____

28. What is the width of this block if the wall thickness is 5/8 inch? _____

29. What is the total length of the cylinder block surface, if the cylinders are 2 31/32 inches in diameter and distance C is 7/8 inch? _____

30. What is the width of the block in problem 29 if the wall thickness is 7/8 inch? _____

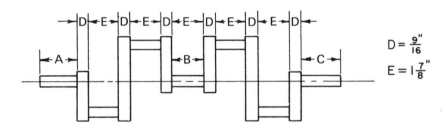

$$D = \frac{9''}{16}$$
$$E = 1\frac{7}{8}''$$

31. What is the length of this crankshaft if main bearing journals A, B, and C are each 1 5/8 inches long? _____

32. If the crankshaft is 15 3/8 inches long and the main bearing journals A and C are 1 7/16 inches long, what is the length of the center main bearing journal B? _____

33. Twelve 7/16-inch diameter holes are drilled in a straight line leaving 3/4 inch between the edges of the holes and at each end. What length piece is necessary? _____

34. If 9 holes are drilled in a straight line with a center-to-center distance of 1 15/32 inches and 2 5/8 inches allowed between each end and the center of the end holes, what length piece is necessary? _____

35. A man uses 48 3/4 gallons of gasoline on a trip. At $.42 9/10 per gallon, how much does he spend for gasoline? _____

Unit 9   DIVISION OF FRACTIONS

BASIC PRINCIPLES OF DIVISION

- Study unit 10 in *Basic Mathematics Simplified* for the principles of division as applied to fractions.

- Apply the principles of division to the automotive field by solving the Review Problems which follow.

REVIEW PROBLEMS

1. What is the distance (center-to-center) between the holes in the sketch if they are equally spaced and A is 21 1/4 inches?   _____

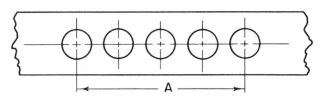

EXHAUST MANIFOLD

2. If A is 18 1/2 inches, what is the center-to-center distance between holes?   _____

3. If A is 7 5/8 inches, what is the center-to-center distance between holes?   _____

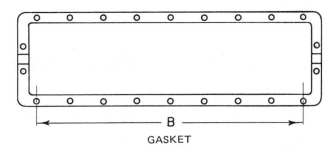

GASKET

4. If the gasket holes are equally spaced and B is 22 1/2 inches, what is the center-to-center distance between holes?   _____

5. If in the gasket, distance B is 16 7/8 inches, what is the center-to-center distance between holes?   _____

6. If 2/3 of an hour is the average time for greasing a car, how many cars can be greased in an 8-hour day?   _____

7. If the spark plugs are cleaned on twenty-one cars in 5 1/4 hours, what is the average time spent on each car?   _____

8. A certain size copper tubing weighs 1/3 pound per foot. How many feet are there in a roll weighing 20 1/2 pounds?   _____

9. A garage buys a fifty-foot roll of 5/8-inch heater hose. How many cars can be repaired if 12 1/2 feet of hose are required for each car? _____

10. A car uses 75 1/2 inches of TVRS wire. If the 8 wires are of equal length, how many inches of wire are there on each spark plug? _____

11. An automobile jack raises the car 3/16 inch for each stroke of the lever. How many strokes of the lever are required to lift the car 3 3/4 inches? _____

12. A garageman has an oil barrel that contains 53 3/4 gallons. If his sales average 10 3/4 gallons a day, how many days will the oil last? _____

13. A customer drives his car 103 miles and uses 5 3/4 gallons of gas. How many miles does he average per gallon of gas? _____

14. At a speedometer reading of 100 miles, the gasoline gage on a car registers 3 1/2 gallons. At the speedometer reading of 1100 miles, the gage reads 4 1/4 gallons. If the owner has had 65 gallons of gasoline placed in the tank during this period, what is the average number of miles this car has traveled per gallon? _____

15. At an average rate of 33 1/2 miles per hour, how many hours does it take to drive 410 3/8 miles? _____

16. How many 4 7/8-inch lengths of radiator hose can be cut from a 3-foot piece of 1 7/16-inch hose? _____

17. If a mechanic is paid $10.00 for 4 3/4 hours of work what is the hourly rate? _____

18. How many times is the nut revolved to take up 1/2 inch on a 1/4 inch—28 NF bolt? _____

19. How many times is the nut revolved to take up 1/2 inch on a 1/4 inch—20 NC bolt? _____

20. Find the number of turns necessary to take up 3/8 inch on a 3/4-inch —16 NF bolt. _____

21. Distance A is 2 1/4 inches. Distance B is 1 3/8 inches. What is the cylinder bore if C is 36 1/8 inches? _____

22. If A is 2 1/2 inches, B is 1 1/8 inches, and C is 30 1/8 inches, what is the cylinder bore? _____

23. When taking stock inventory, a mechanic weighs 25 of the 1/4-inch — 20 nuts which weigh 15 ounces. The total weight of all the 1/4-inch — 20 nuts is 5 pounds, 13 ounces. How many nuts are there? _____

24. What is the crank throw when the stroke is 4 3/16 inches?

    _____

25. What is the crank throw when the stroke is 3 3/4 inches?

    _____

26. How many pieces of safety wire 7/8 inch long can be cut from a piece 7 inches long?

    _____

CRANK THROW

27. How many pieces of safety wire 1 5/16 inches long can be cut from a piece 13 1/8 inches long? _____

28. How many 7 3/8-inch pieces of copper tubing can be cut from a 10-foot length? _____

29. A lot of bushings costs $4.00. If the price per bushing is $.04 1/2, how many bushings are in the lot? _____

30. Two 10 foot lengths of ignition wire are cut up into pieces 6 3/4 inches long. How many pieces are made? _____

31. How many shims 3 7/8 inches long can be made from 20 shim strips, each 3 feet long? _____

32. If 9 2/3 yards of gasket material cost $19.00, how much does it cost per yard? _____

33. How many 16 3/8-inch lengths can be cut from a 10-foot length of wire? _____

34. If 7 3/4 dozen of small fittings cost $7.00, what is the cost per dozen? _____

35. How many 1 3/4-inch machine bolt blanks can be cut from a 5-foot length of stock? Allow 7/32 inch for waste on each blank. _____

36. If a man averages 45 3/4 miles per hour on a trip, how long does it take him to travel 571 7/8 miles? _____

37. A lot of bolts costs $5.25. At $.05 1/4 each, how many bolts are there in the lot? _____

Unit 10 FRACTIONAL EQUIVALENTS

BASIC PRINCIPLES OF FRACTIONAL EQUIVALENTS

- Study unit 12 in *Basic Mathematics Simplified* for the principles of fractional equivalents as applied to decimals.

- Apply the principles of fractional equivalents to the automotive field by solving the Review Problems which follow.

REVIEW PROBLEMS

1. What is the nearest fractional drill size to the following decimal measurements:

.880 inch	.618 inch
.555 inch	.815 inch
.230 inch	.439 inch

   _____

   _____

   _____

   _____

   _____

   _____

2. What is the next 1/16 inch larger than .750 inch? _____

3. What is the next 1/16 inch larger than .250 inch? _____

4. What is the next 1/8 inch larger than .625 inch? _____

5. What is the next 1/8 inch larger than .375 inch? _____

6. What is the size of a drill 1/16 inch larger than 1/2 inch? _____

7. What is the size of a drill 1/4 inch larger than .375 inch? _____

8. What is the diameter of a 3/8-inch hole drilled 3/16 inch oversize? _____

9. What is the diameter of a 3/4-inch hole drilled 1/16 inch oversize? _____

10. What is the next 1/16 inch larger than 5/8 inch? _____

Unit 11   ADDITION OF DECIMALS

BASIC PRINCIPLES OF ADDITION

- Study unit 13 in *Basic Mathematics Simplified* for the principles of addition as applied to decimals.

- Apply the principles of addition to the automotive field by solving the Review Problems which follow.

REVIEW PROBLEMS

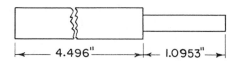

1. What is the total length of the clutch plate pilot tool shown above? _____

2. A valve will expand in length when it is heated. The length of valve when cold is 7.8750 inches; it expands .0035 inch when hot. What is its length when hot? _____

3. If a 6.70 x 15-inch tire costs $14.35 and the Federal Excise Tax (FET) is $1.65, what is the total cost of the tire? _____

4. A customer at a gasoline station buys 1 quart of oil for $.60, polish for $1.48, and a polish cloth for $.79. How much does he pay the attendant? _____

5. What is the total amount of a bill itemized as follows: compressor seal $6.45, refrigerant $5.50, clutch brush set $2.70, dye trace solution $2.25, and labor $16.85? _____

6. A starter ring gear that measures 14.675 inches inside diameter will expand .075 inch on the diameter when heated. What is its diameter when heated? _____

7. Five thousandths of an inch are to be ground out of a bore that measures three and eight hundred seventy-five thousandths inches. What will be the reground size, stating answer numerically? _____

8. What is the distance from center of the connecting rod bearing to the top of the piston? _____

9. What is the length of the piston? _____

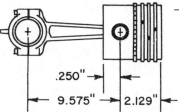

.250"
9.575"   2.129"

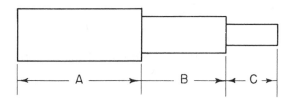

10. A = 1.067 inches, B = .96 inch, C = .0875 inch. What is the total length? _____

11. A = 2.3005 inches, B = 1.030 inches, C = .8055 inch.   What is the total length? _____

12. A = One and seventy-five thousandths inches.

B = One and four hundred seventy-five hundred thousandths inches.

C = Eight hundred forty-five thousandths of an inch.

What is the total length of the pin shown above, stated numerically? _____

13. A piston pin wears a groove in a cylinder wall .012 inch deep on one side and .0075 inch on the other.   What size is the cylinder rebored in order to clean up the bore if the original size was 3.125 inches? _____

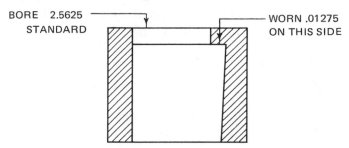

BORE   2.5625 ——————
STANDARD

WORN .01275
ON THIS SIDE

14. What size should the rebore be to straighten up the bore as illustrated above? _____

15. If the chassis frame of a car is .250 inch thick, the spring hanger is .375 inch thick, and it takes .050 inch to head the rivet, what is the total length of a rivet needed to fasten these two pieces together? _____

Note: The term oversize as used in connection with parts having a circular section, such as pistons, piston pins, and cylinders, refers to an increase in the diameter of the part from the original or standard size.

The term clearance as used in connection with parts having a circular section refers to the difference between the two diameters of the parts fitted together.

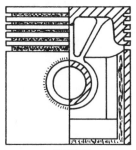

PISTON

16. The standard size of a certain piston pin is .625 inch, the oversize is .005 inch greater; what is the actual size? _____

17. A cylinder bore is ground .020 inch large.   The standard size is 3.375 inches in diameter; what is the size of the rebored cylinder? _____

18. An aluminum piston expands .0055 inch when hot. This, then, is the clearance which is allowed. What is its diameter after expansion if its standard diameter is 3.6875 inches?   _____

19. A certain cylinder is 3.375 inches in diameter standard size. It is ground .005 inch oversize. What is the size of the rebored cylinder?   _____

20. A hole for a piston pin, originally .8175 inch in diameter, has worn .0012 inch. What size is the hole?   _____

21. What size is the bushing reamed for a spring bolt measuring 0.85 inch in diameter, if .002 inch is allowed for clearance?   _____

22. A standard cylinder bore is 3.4375 inches in diameter. If .0285 inch is removed from diameter by grinding, what is the size after being reground?   _____

23. A cylinder bore originally measured three and six hundred eighty-seven thousandths, but was worn six thousandths of an inch. What is the greatest diameter of bore? State answer numerically.   _____

24. A mechanic replaces a set of standard piston pins which measure .875 inch in diameter with a set .015 inch oversize. What do the new pins measure?   _____

25. On a honing job, it is desired to replace the original pistons, which measure 3.125 inches, with pistons .015 inch oversize. What size will the honed cylinder be, if .002-inch clearance is allowed?   _____

26. An aluminum piston expands .0055 inch in diameter when heated. What is its size after expansion, if its standard size is 3.1875 inches in diameter?   _____

27. A piston pin scores a cylinder wall .012 inch deep on one side and .007 inch deep on the other. What is the size of the bore, reground, if the standard size is 3.125 inches? (Standard oversizes for reboring are: .010, .020, .030, .040, .050, and .060 inches.)

28. What is the outside diameter measurement of a tire with a 15-inch rim size and a 6.70-inch diameter shoe?   _____

29. What is the outside diameter of a 6.50 x 14-inch tire?   _____

30. What is the outside diameter of a 7.75 x 14-inch tire?   _____

Unit 12 SUBTRACTION OF DECIMALS

BASIC PRINCIPLES OF SUBTRACTION

- Study unit 14 in *Basic Mathematics Simplified* for the principles of subtraction as applied to decimals.

- Apply the principles of subtraction to the automotive field by solving the Review Problems which follow.

REVIEW PROBLEMS

1. How much must be cut from a shackle bushing measuring 2.375 inches in length to fit a spring 2.125 inches wide? _____

2. If .022 inch is removed from a pin 1.25 inches long, what length is left? _____

3. The standard width of a certain piston ring is .1875 inch. The micrometer reading is .184 inch. How much is it worn? _____

4. An aluminum piston when cold measures 3.875 inches. When heated, it measures 3.8815 inches. What is the amount of expansion? _____

5. Two pistons have diameters of 2.8125 inches and 2.875 inches respectively. What is the difference in their diameters? _____

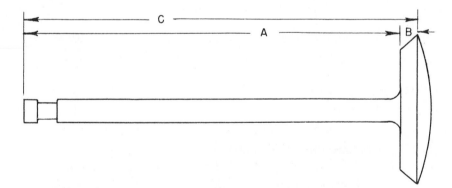

6. Determine dimension A numerically if B is three hundred nine thousandths of an inch, C is four and seventy-five thousandths inches. _____

7. The difference in the sizes of a new 3.375-inch diameter piston and a worn one is .0185 inch. What is the size of the old piston? _____

8. A customer is charged $4.60 for labor and $2.21 for parts for a repair job done on his car. When paying this bill, what change should he receive from a ten dollar bill? _____

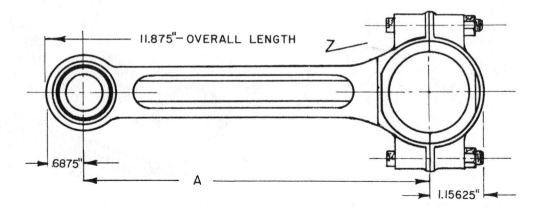

9. What is the center-to-center distance A between the holes? _____

10. If the overall length is 10.0000 inches and the other two dimensions are .750 inch and 1.0050 inches, what is dimension A? _____

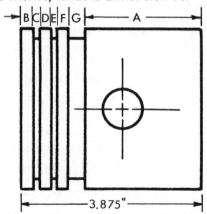

11. Find length A of the skirt; the other dimensions are as follows: b = .1875, c = .125, d = .1875, e = .125, f = .1875, g = .250 inches. _____

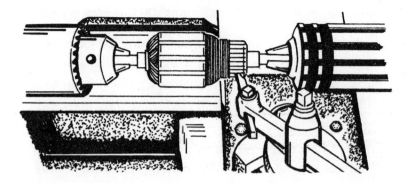

12. A generator commutator 2 inches in diameter is turned down on a lathe, the tool taking a cut .0625 inch deep. What is the finished diameter? _____

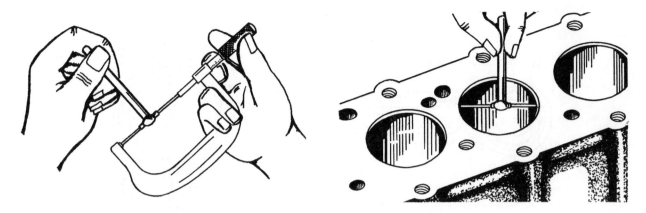

13. A .0015-inch feeler gage is placed between the cylinder wall and the piston. If the cylinder bore is 3.5 inches, what is the diameter of the piston? _____

14. The standard size of a bore is 2.875 inches. It is ground to 2.877 inches. What amount is the diameter increased? _____

15. What amount must be removed from a piston that is 2.883 inches in diameter, if it is to fit in a bore 2.875 inches with a clearance of .002 inch? _____

16. ·A piston measures 3.8825 inches. It is to be placed in a bore measuring 3.875 inches with .0025-inch clearance. To what size should the piston be ground? _____

17. How many thousandths of an inch must be removed from a bore that is standard at 2.875 inches to give it an oversize of 2.915 inches in diameter? _____

18. A cylinder bore that is out-of-round measures 2.8125 inches one way of the bore and 2.8160 inches the other way. How much is the cylinder out-of-round? _____

19. A cylinder measures .020 inch over standard. The standard is 3.375 inches. What is the piston size for this cylinder, allowing .002-inch clearance? _____

20. When ordering pistons, the jobber always wants to know the exact size of the renewed cylinders. If the cylinder is 4 inches in diameter and is ground .030 inches oversize, what is the actual size of the piston that will be received from the jobber, if this product requires .002-inch clearance? _____

21. During the operation of finishing a piston to a specified size of 2.6835 inches, a test measurement reading is 2.685 inches. How much more stock must be removed? _____

22. A .375-inch valve stem at point of greatest wear is .0175 inch undersize. What is its diameter at this point? _____

Unit 13   MULTIPLICATION OF DECIMALS

BASIC PRINCIPLES OF MULTIPLICATION

- Study unit 15 in *Basic Mathematics Simplified* for the principles of multiplication as applied to decimals.

- Apply the principles of multiplication to the automotive field by solving the Review Problems which follow.

REVIEW PROBLEMS

Note: It is often necessary to express decimals to the nearest fraction of an inch; for example, express .7 inch to the nearest 1/16 inch.

$$.7 \times 16/16 = 11.2/16 = 11/16 \text{ nearest}$$

Change the following decimals to the nearest indicated scale measurement:

1. .31 inch to nearest 1/16 inch   _____

2. .809 inch to nearest 1/16 inch   _____

3. .860 inch to nearest 1/8 inch   _____

4. .781 inch to nearest 1/32 inch   _____

5. .5155 inch to nearest 1/64 inch   _____

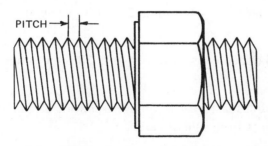

PITCH

6. If the pitch of a thread is .125 inch, how far is a nut moved in 6.5 turns? Express answer as a decimal.   _____

7. Express the answer in problem 6 to the nearest 1/16 inch.   _____

8. If the pitch is .05 inch, how far is a nut moved in 36 turns? (As a decimal)   _____

9. Express the answer in problem 8 to the nearest 1/32 inch.   _____

10. If a machine screw has 12 threads and the pitch is .0625 inch, how long is the screw under the head?   _____

11. Express the answer in problem 10 to the nearest 1/64 inch.   _____

12. A 6-cell storage battery on discharge gives a voltage reading of 1.85 volts per cell. What is the total voltage of the battery?   _____

13. If a 6-cell storage battery shows an average voltage of 2.2 volts per cell, what is the voltage of the battery?   _____

14. A test shows a fully charged storage battery is discharged by a current of 11.25 amperes in 7.2 hours. What is the probable capacity of this battery expressed in ampere-hours? (Ampere-hour equals the product of the amperage discharge rate and the number of hours necessary to discharge the battery.) _____

15. A head gasket set costs $.55 for an air conditioning compressor. The garage uses three sets per week. What does a two-month supply cost? _____

16. Each brush for a certain type (2 brush) generator costs $.65. What will brushes cost to repair six of these generators? _____

17. A set of alternator brushes costs $.65. What will a dozen sets of brushes cost? _____

18. A particular type starter brush costs $1.70 per set (4 brushes). What will eight sets of brushes cost? _____

19. A mechanic receives $1.95 per hour for his services. How much does he earn in 20 hours? _____

20. On a special deal, a garageman is able to purchase power steering hose at $.32 per foot, but to do so he must buy a job lot of 256 3/4 feet. What does he have to pay for this lot of hose? _____

21. At the rate of $.35 1/2 per foot, what does 9 feet 3 inches of radiator hose cost? _____

22. A garageman buys 3 1/4-dozen cans of polish at $.335 per can. What is the total cost? _____

23. A firm sold 114 automobiles last year at an average price of $2785.73. What were the total receipts from sale of cars? _____

24. If the cost of gasoline is $.259 per gallon, what will 369 gallons cost? _____

25. A certain garageman charges $6.60 per hour for his shop labor. What is his charge for a job which requires 12 1/6 hours? _____

26. In a 6-cylinder car, the piston displacement of one cylinder is 36.82 cubic inches. What is the total piston displacement for the motor of this car? _____

27. A man contracts for 36,550 gallons of gasoline at $.193 per gallon. What is the total cost of the gasoline? _____

28. A customer gives a garageman a $20.00 bill in payment for 1 1/2 hours labor at $5.50 per hour and a small replacement part that cost $1.10. What change does the customer receive? _____

29. A repair job requires 4 1/8 days to complete. At $45.50 per day, what is the cost? _____

30. What is the weight of 24 3/4 gallons of gasoline if one gallon weighs 6.56 pounds? _____

31. A gallon of gasoline weighs 6.56 pounds. How much does a gasoline truck weigh that is carrying 450 gallons of gas if the empty truck weighs 4500 pounds? _____

32. What is the cost of a barrel of grease at $.17 1/4 per pound, if the barrel contains 53 1/2 gallons and a gallon weighs 7.44 pounds? _____

33. What is the cost of replacing an air conditioning clutch armature on a car if the cost of material is $10.50 and labor amounts to 1/2 hour at $7.50 per hour? _____

34. A dealer sells 5 quarts of oil at $.60 per quart. The oil cost him $.36 a quart. What is the profit on the sale? _____

35. What is the profit on 450 gallons of gasoline which costs $.223 and sells for $.269 per gallon? _____

36. What is the cost of 720 gallons of gasoline at $.207 per gallon? _____

37. The weight of a certain piston and connecting rod assembly is 12.65 ounces. What is the weight of 8 such assemblies?

_____

COMPRESSION RINGS

PISTON

OIL RING

CONNECTING ROD

38. What is the cost of a tuneup on an 8-cylinder car if the following material is used (cost of material, less labor): spark plugs, $1.08 each; points, $2.20; condenser, $1.03; and distributor rotor, $1.33?

_____

39. A certain type of metal weighs 1.9 pounds per square foot. If 359 square feet of this metal are used to build a truck body, what is the total weight of the metal used? _____

40. What is the cost at $.16 1/2 per pound of the metal required in problem 39? _____

41. A mechanic overhauls a power steering pump, using the following material: gasket set, $1.47; 2 quarts of oil, $.95 each; 2 hose clamps, $.35 each; and 2 hours labor, $6.50 per hour. What is the total cost of the job? _____

42. A speedometer is repaired on a certain car. The following material is used: main frame assembly, $5.65; odometer, $7.00; cross shaft, $1.25; cable core, $2.96; and three hours labor, $7.00 per hour. What is the cost of the job? _____

Unit 14   DIVISION OF DECIMALS

BASIC PRINCIPLES OF DIVISION

- Study unit 16 in *Basic Mathematics Simplified* for the principles of division as applied to decimals.

- Apply the principles of division to the automotive field by solving the Review Problems which follow.

REVIEW PROBLEMS

1. A man rents his truck for $26.50 per day. What is the rental price per hour, on the basis of an 8-hour day?   _____

2. What is the average mileage per gallon of gasoline, if a car runs 843.7 miles on 45 gallons?   _____

3. What is the average speed in miles per hour of a car that is driven 340 miles in 7.75 hours?   _____

4. A truck driver charges $.24 per parcel for delivery. He earned $30.72 one day. How many parcels did he deliver?   _____

5. A workman's pay check is $82.20 per week of 5 days. What is his rate of pay, per hour, figuring 8 hours per day?   _____

6. The cost of maintaining 12 small trucks for a year is $3,745.00. What is the average cost per week, for one truck?   _____

7. If an auto, on a certain trip, totaling 372.6 miles averages 38.5 miles per hour, how long does it take to make this trip?   _____

8. A set of brakes costs $38.00 to reline. What is the cost, per mile, if a set lasts 38,000 miles?   _____

9. If 15 gallons of gasoline weigh 98.4 pounds, what does one gallon weigh?   _____

10. A tire of a certain size costs $48.00. If it is used 17,762 miles, what is the cost per mile?   _____

11. How many quarts of oil are needed on a trip of 2,525 miles if the average consumption is 1 quart each 425 miles?   _____

12. A car is driven 38,460 miles in one year at a cost of $2,115.34. What is the cost per mile?   _____

13. A tire costs $28.70 and is used on a car 14,235 miles. What is the cost per mile?   _____

14. A used car dealer sells 34 automobiles and the total sales amount to $58,750.00. What is the average price of each car? _____

15. A set of spark plugs costing $6.60 is used 11, 512 miles. What is the cost per mile? _____

10 CUBIC INCHES

50 CUBIC INCHES

DISPLACEMENT 40 CUBIC INCHES

16. The piston displacement of a certain 8-cylinder engine is 452.8 cubic inches. What is the displacement of one cylinder? _____

17. The distance around the outside of a tire (circumference) is 92.250 inches. How many times will the tire turn over in 500 feet? _____

18. A pail of grease contains 42.5 pounds and costs $5.30. What is the cost per pound? _____

19. A number of pieces of heater hose totaling 42 feet cost $7.85. What is the cost per foot? _____

20. The cost of 22 point sets is $31.90. What is the cost per set? _____

21. A space on a steel frame is 14.885 inches long. If this space is divided into 4 equal parts, how long is each space? _____

22. A man is paid $21.33 for a 185.5 mile trip in his automobile. What is his charge per mile? _____

23. A car owner's garage bill comes to $85.80. He pays one half of the bill in cash and the remainder in five equal payments. What is the amount of each of the monthly payments? _____

24. The total displacement in an 8-cylinder engine is 352.8 inches. What is the displacement in each cylinder? _____

25. On a certain trip, an automobile travels at an average rate of 46.5 miles per hour, and at the end of the trip, it has covered 227 miles. How much time is required to make the trip? _____

Unit 15   READING OF OUTSIDE AND INSIDE MICROMETERS

BASIC PRINCIPLES OF MICROMETER READING

- Study unit 19 in *Basic Mathematics Simplified* for the principles of micrometer reading.
- Apply the principles of micrometer reading to the automotive field by solving the Review Problems which follow.

REVIEW PROBLEMS

Fill in the following tables showing how you would set the micrometers to obtain the readings given.

1-inch Outside Micrometer

Prob. No.	Reading in Inches	Number of numbered divisions on the barrel	Number of un-numbered divisions on the barrel	Number of thimble divisions
1	.875			
2	.3125			
3	.21875			
4	.893			
5	.666			
6	.008			
7	.077			

Inside Micrometer

Prob. No.	Reading in Inches	Size of extension rod in Inches	1/2-inch spacing collar		No. of numbered divisions	No. of unnumbered divisions	No. of thimble divisions
			Yes	No			
8	2.625						
9	6.1875						
10	4.34375						
11	3.750						
12	2.555						
13	4.067						
14	5.899						
15	3.999						

Unit 16 CUMULATIVE REVIEW OF FRACTIONS AND DECIMALS

1. If a truck driver travels a distance of 2,026 3/4 miles in 5 1/2 days, what average distance does he drive each day?   _____

2. A garage owner buys 35,480 gallons of gasoline at $.289 per gallon. If he sells the gasoline for $.339 per gallon, what is his gross profit?   _____

3. If the minimum width for repair stalls in a garage is 8 3/4 feet, how many stalls can be built in an area 38 feet wide?   _____

4. What is the weight of the gasoline in a tank which holds 21.8 gallons, if one gallon weighs 6.56 pounds?   _____

5. A motor with a standard bore of 3 3/16 inches is rebored to .050 inch oversize. What does the new bore measure?   _____

6. Six piston pins, .005 inch oversize, are required for a certain job. The standard size is 11/16 inch. What do the new pins measure?   _____

7. If a cylinder 3 1/2 inches in diameter, as shown in the above sketch, is rebored .030 inches oversize, what does the finished diameter read on the micrometer? _____

8. In "feeling" the ring fit in the piston ring groove as shown in the sketch, a .002-inch feeler fits snugly. What is the width of the groove if a 3/16-inch ring is being used?

9. The holes in the frame holding the side member to the crossmember have become worn and enlarged. Originally, they were 3/8 inch. They now measure about .450 inch in diameter. Find the difference between the original diameter of the hole and what it now measures to the nearest 1/16 inch.   _____

10. A king-bolt measures 7/8 inch in diameter. If .0005 inch is the clearance for a fit in the bushing, what is the reamer setting to the nearest .0001 inch?   _____

11. What fractional size bolt is used in a .314-inch hole? (Express the answer to nearest 1/16 inch.)   _____

12. If a car travels 1,296 1/2 miles on a certain trip and uses 75 3/4 gallons of gasoline, what is the average mileage per gallon?   _____

13. What is the cost of the gasoline used in problem 12 at $.269 per gallon?   _____

14. Mr. Smith kept account of the expenses on his car for one year. Based on the following data, how much is his operating cost?

    800 gallons gasoline, $.29 per gallon (average); 1 oil filter (every second oil change), $3.40 each; 2 pints differential lube, $.40 per pint; 1 quart transmission fluid, $1.00 per quart; 1 can rust inhibitor (radiator), $1.50 per can; 1 power steering belt, $2.50 each; 12 changes of engine oil (see note), $.65 per quart; 6 grease jobs, $2.50 each; miscellaneous repair charges, $29.40 total; estimated tire wear, $35.00 total. (Depreciation not considered.)

    Note: 5 quarts with filter change; 4 quarts without filter change.   _____

15. If Mr. Smith's car is valued at $1,500.00 and he allows one-fourth of the value per year depreciation, what is the operating cost per mile, including the expenses of problem 14 if the car is driven 14,954 miles?   _____

16. What is the cost of 350 pounds of pressure grease if 1 pound costs $.24?   _____

17. How many times can a grease gun that holds 34 pounds be filled from a 225-pound drum of lubricant?   _____

18. The capacity of a transmission is 4 1/2 pints. If 1 pint of gear oil weighs 1 1/16 pounds, how many transmissions of the same capacity can be filled from a barrel containing 377 pounds?   _____

19. Compute the total cost of the following articles: 4 large grease guns, $17.17 each; 6 small grease guns, $4.09 each; 100 lubricator fittings (straight), $.06 each; 75 lubricator fittings (120 degrees), $.22 each; 16 lubricator fittings (90 degrees), $.22 each.   _____

20. Compute the total cost of the following list of lubricating supplies: one 250-pound drum gear compound, $.19 1/4 per pound; one 95-pound drum universal joint lube., $.26 per pound; one 5 gallon can oil, $4.25 per gallon.   _____

21. What is the net cost of the supplies in problem 20, if a refund for the return of the empty containers is as follows: 250-pound drum, $1.12; 95-pound drum, $.80.   _____

22. The price charged a customer for having a car lubricated is $1.60. The operator receives $.65, and the cost of material is $.28. What amount is left to cover overhead and profit?   _____

23. How many cars like that in problem 22 does the operator have to grease to earn $5.20?   _____

24. What is the micrometer reading for a piece of 7/8-inch diameter stock? _____

25. What is the micrometer reading of a wrist pin on a certain model car which measures 13/16 inch? _____

26. If a piece of round stock is 5/8 inch, what is the micrometer reading? _____

27. An automobile has a wrist pin 15/16 inch in diameter. How many thousandths does this read on the micrometer? _____

28. A certain shaft size is given as 55/64 inch. What does this measure on a micrometer? _____

29. Express the measurement of a 3/4-inch wrist pin to the nearest .001 inch. _____

30. A wrist pin is 3/4-inch in diameter. What figures represent the micrometer reading for the diameter of this pin? _____

31. A certain wrist pin measures .8594 inch in diameter. What is the fractional dimension to the nearest 1/64 inch? _____

32. The micrometer reading for the diameter of the wrist pin in the sketch is .875 inch. What is this dimension, expressed in fractions to the nearest 1/32 inch? _____

33. Express 1/16 inch decimally to the nearest .001 inch. _____

34. A certain stock measures .875 inch in diameter. What does this measure in 1/16 inch, with an outside caliper and a scale? _____

35. What does a piece of 26/32-inch bar stock measure to the nearest .001 inch with a micrometer? _____

36. To what reading is a micrometer set for 51/64 inch? _____

37. The diameter of a certain wrist pin is 49/64 inch. How is this written to the nearest .001 inch? _____

38. Express 31/32 inch to the nearest .001 inch. _____

39. Give the micrometer reading for a piece of 3/64-inch sheet metal.   _____

40. How many .001 inch are in 1/64 inch?   _____

41. What fraction is equal to .03125 inch?

   Note: When it is necessary to order oversize piston pins, the mechanic needs only to give the number of thousandths above the standard size piston pin for the type car he is working on. For example, 7/8-inch standard piston pin expressed in thousandths, is .875 inch. If it is necessary to ream for a piston pin which is .005 inch oversize, this piston pin is .880 inch in diameter. However, the mechanic will simply say it is 5 over 7/8 inch, meaning the oversize piston pin needed is five thousandths larger than the 7/8-inch (.875-inch) pin which is the standard size for this car.   _____

42. Careful inspection of a piston shows that the piston pin bosses are reamed .003 inch oversize when fitting new piston pins. If the standard size pin removed measures .750 inch, how does the mechanic order the new piston pin?   _____

43. The standard size piston pin for a certain car is 11/16 inch. When a piston pin is taken out of this car it measures .6895 inch.

   a.   Had an oversize pin been fitted previously in this car?   _____

   b.   If your answer to (a) is yes, how many thousandths oversize was the pin?   _____

44. If in problem 43 it is necessary to ream a .008 inch larger hole for the piston pin, how does the mechanic order the new pin?   _____

45. What is the most probable fractional size piston pin if the micrometer measurement is .906 inch?   _____

46. If a hole .911 inch in diameter is reamed for a new piston pin in problem 45, how many thousandths oversize is it?   _____

47. How is the size of a piston pin which measures .635 inch designated?   _____

48. What is the diameter, as measured by a micrometer, for piston pins ordered as 3 over 7/8 inch?

   Note: The same term is used when ordering interchangeable connecting rod bearing shells. However, the bearing shell is ordered undersize to compensate for the wear of the crankpin.   _____

49. What does 5 under 1 5/8 inches mean when ordering bearing shells?   _____

50. How are bearing shells .010 inch undersize ordered for a car with a 1.875-inch diameter standard crankpin?   _____

TABLE OF TAP DRILL SIZES						
National Coarse				**National Fine**		
Thread Size	**Diam. of Hole in Inches**	**Drill**		**Thread Size**	**Diam. of Hole in Inches**	**Drill**
1/4 −20	.201	#7		1/4 −28	.213	#3
5/16 −18	.257	"F"		5/16 −24	.272	"I"
3/8 −16	.313	5/16		3/8 −24	.332	"Q"
7/16 −14	.368	"U"		7/16 −20	.391	25/64
1/2 −13	.422	27/64		1/2 −20	.453	29/64
9/16 −12	.484	31/64		9/16 −18	.516	33/64
5/8 −11	.531	17/32		5/8 −18	.578	37/64
11/16 −11	.594	19/32		11/16 −16	.625	5/8
3/4 −10	.656	21/32		3/4 −16	.688	11/16
13/16 −10	.719	23/32		7/8 −14	.813	13/16
7/8 − 9	.766	49/64		1 −14	.938	15/16
15/16 − 9	.828	53/64				
1 − 8	.875	7/8				

51. If threads are stripped in a hole which takes a 1/4-inch − 20 NC cap screw and the hole is drilled and tapped for the next larger size −

    a.   What size hole is drilled? _____

    b.   What number drill is used? _____

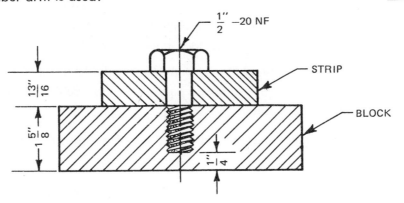

52. If it is necessary to drill through the strip into the block without going nearer than 1/4 inch to the bottom of the block, what depth is the hole drilled? _____

53. What size is used for the hole through the strip? _____

54. What size drill is used for the hole in the block? _____

55. If a 5/8-inch − 18 NF cap screw must pass through the strip into a tapped hole in the block, what size drill is used for the hole which is to be tapped? _____

Automotive electrical cable is made of stranded wires for flexibility. The number of strands used varies but is usually 7, 19, 37, 61, 91, or 127.   In ordering cable the diameter is expressed as a gage size.   The following table gives the gage sizes:

Wire Diameter Inches	American Wire Gage	Circular Mil Area	Wire Diameter Inches	American Wire Gage	Circular Mil Area
.4600	0000	211,600	.0284	21	810.1
.4096	000	167,800	.0253	22	642.4
.3648	00	133,100	.0225	23	509.5
.3249	0	105,500	.0201	24	404.0
.2893	1	83,690	.0179	25	320.4
.2576	2	66,370	.0159	26	254.1
.2294	3	52,640	.0142	27	201.5
.2043	4	41,740	.0126	28	159.8
.1620	· 6	26,250	.0112	29	126.7
.1285	8	16,510	.0100	30	100.5
.1019	10	10,380	.0089	31	79.70
.0808	12	6,530	.0079	32	63.21
.0640	14	4,107	.0070	33	50.13
.0508	16	2,583	.0063	34	39.75
.0403	18	1,624	.0056	35	31.52
.0319	20	1,002	.0050	36	25.0

Note: The circular mil is a unit of area used in electrical work.   The values under the column headed "Circular Mil Area " in the chart, give a comparison of the amount of copper in each wire.

56. A cable has 19 strands of wire, each strand measuring .0112 in diameter (#29 gage).   What size cable is ordered to replace this cable? Give answer as the nearest gage number.   _____

57. What is the nearest gage number for a cable of seven strands of #18 wire?   _____

58. Of what gage single strands does a 37-stranded motor cable #1 gage consist?   _____

59. Approximately how many times more copper is there in a #1-gage wire than in a #4-gage wire?   _____

60. What gage is a cable which is composed of 61 strands of .010-inch diameter wire?   _____

61. The diameter of a #36 wire is half as much as the diameter of a #30 wire, but how many times more copper does the #30 wire have?   _____

Unit 17 FRACTIONAL EQUIVALENTS

BASIC PRINCIPLES OF FRACTIONAL EQUIVALENTS

- Study unit 25 in *Basic Mathematics Simplified* for the principles of fractional equivalents as applied to percentage.
- Apply the principles of fractional equivalents to the automotive field by solving the Review Problems which follow.

REVIEW PROBLEMS

Give the fractional equivalent of each of the following percentages (%):

1.	25%	_____	6. 12 1/2%	_____
2.	40%	_____	7. 66 2/3%	_____
3.	10%	_____	8. 16 2/3%	_____
4.	75%	_____	9. 5%	_____
5.	60%	_____	10. 8 1/3%	_____

11. In a shipment of one gross (144) automobile headlight lamps, 50% of the lamps is found broken. How many damaged lamps are there? _____

12. How many damaged lamps are there in a shipment of 200 in which 25% is found broken? _____

13. In a shipment of 500 lamps, 10% is broken. How many are broken? _____

14. In a shipment of 80 lamps, 12 1/2% is broken. How many are broken? _____

15. In a shipment of 120 lamps, 16 2/3% is broken. How many are broken? _____

16. What percent of 64 is 16? _____

17. What percent of 25 is 5? _____

18. What percent of 150 is 15? _____

19. What percent of 160 is 20? _____

20. What percent of 120 is 6? _____

21. What percent of 27 is 9? _____

22. Fifteen piston pins out of 75 are rejected. What percent is rejected? _____

23. In problem 22, what percent is accepted? _____

Unit 18   SIMPLE PERCENTAGE

BASIC PRINCIPLES OF SIMPLE PERCENTAGE

- Study unit 26 in *Basic Mathematics Simplified* for the principles of simple percentage.

- Apply the principles of simple percentage to the automotive field by solving the Review Problems which follow.

REVIEW PROBLEMS

1. A mechanic earning $2.40 per hour receives a 10% increase in pay. What is his new hourly rate? _____

2. If a mechanic's hourly rate is $2.30 and this is increased 16 2/3%, what is the new hourly rate? _____

3. How much more per week will an 8% increase in wages mean to a mechanic who is receiving $64.00 per week? _____

4. A repair shop offers a 5% bonus to mechanics completing jobs in a specified time. If the hourly rate of pay is $2.16, how much more money does a mechanic make in a 40-hour week if he is entitled to the bonus? _____

5. A repair shop reduces its working hours from 44 to 40 without reducing the weekly rate of pay of the mechanics. To what percentage increase in pay is this equivalent? _____

6. If it requires 4 hours to rebush the front end of a car, what does the mechanic receive for his flat rate work, if the customer pays $3.25 per hour for the man's time and the man receives 75% of what the customer pays? _____

7. A mechanic receives $2.80 per hour for his services. He receives a raise in pay of 12 1/2 percent. What is his new hourly rate of pay? _____

8. Six quarts of alcohol are used in the cooling system of a car which has a capacity of 5 1/2 gallons. What percentage of the solution is alcohol? _____

9. Babbitt metal for severe service is composed of approximately 90% tin, 5% copper and 5% antimony. If 25 pounds of babbitt metal are required, how much copper is necessary? _____

10. Ten pounds of antimony is sufficient for how many pounds of babbitt metal? _____

11. How much tin is necessary for 42 pounds of babbitt metal? _____

12. If 1% of the supply of gasoline is lost per day through evaporation, how many gallons are lost each day from 4 tanks each holding 2,500 gallons? _____

13. The capacity of a cooling system is 16 quarts. Using denatured alcohol as an antifreeze, to withstand a temperature of 8°F., the minimum solution must be 25% alcohol and 75% water. How much alcohol is required to take care of this cooling system? Express answer in quarts. _____

Using the following percentage values, fill in the chart showing the number of pints of alcohol necessary in cooling systems of various capacities to protect against freezing at the temperatures shown.

Capacity of Cooling System	10°F 27% Alcohol Pints Alcohol	0°F 35% Alcohol Pints Alcohol	-10°F 42% Alcohol Pints Alcohol	-20°F 50% Alcohol Pints Alcohol
2 gallons	14.	19.	24.	29.
3 gallons	15.	20.	25.	30.
4 gallons	16.	21.	26.	31.
5 gallons	17.	22.	27.	32.
6 gallons	18.	23.	28.	33.

Fill in the chart for Prestone antifreeze using the information shown below. The values which are missing and which you will compute, show the temperature to which the cooling system is protected against freezing.

Use values in this chart.

Percent Prestone	Protection to
20	+16°F
25	+10°F
30	+ 4°F
33 1/3	0°F
40	-12°F
50	-34°F
60	-62°F

Gallons Capacity	Gallons of Prestone Used				
	1	1 1/2	2	2 1/2	3
2 1/2	34.	35.			
3	36.	37.			
4	38.		39.		
5	40.	41.	42.	43.	44.
6		45.	46.		47.

Check your values with the Prestone Chart.

Unit 19   GRADES (INCLINES)

BASIC PRINCIPLES OF GRADES

- Review units 25 and 26 in *Basic Mathematics Simplified* for the principles of percentage.
- Apply the principles of percentage to the automotive field by solving the Review Problems which follow.

REVIEW PROBLEMS

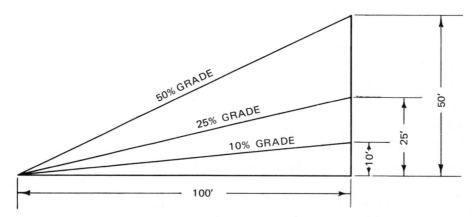

Note: A grade is expressed in terms of percentage and means so many feet rise or fall in a given distance measured in a horizontal direction.

1. What is the percentage grade where a rise of 30 feet occurs in a horizontal distance of 100 feet?   _____

2. What is the grade of a hill which rises 40 feet in a horizontal distance of 200 feet?   _____

3. What is the grade if a slope rises 1 foot for each 20 feet?   _____

4. A 66 2/3% grade is as steep as a car could possibly climb because gravity overcomes traction at this angle.   If an automobile ramp spans a distance of 60 feet, what is the maximum height A as shown in sketch?   _____

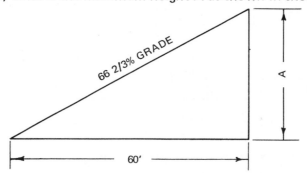

5. What is the grade if an 18-inch rise occurs in a horizontal distance of 10 feet?   _____

6. What is the grade in a rise of 1 foot over a horizontal distance of 1 foot?   _____

Unit 20   DISCOUNTS

BASIC PRINCIPLES OF DISCOUNTS

- Study unit 30 in *Basic Mathematics Simplified* for the principles of discounts.
- Apply the principles of discount to the automotive field by solving the Review Problems which follow.

REVIEW PROBLEMS

1. A mechanic purchases 7 1/2 feet of 13/32-inch air-conditioning hose at 95¢ per foot. He receives a discount of 40%. What does he pay for this hose?   _____

2. A rear seat speaker switch costs 90¢. If the discount is 33 1/3%, what is the net cost of the switch?   _____

3. In lots of six, 3/8-inch compression fittings cost 55¢ each. What is the cost of 6 fittings if the discount is 33 1/3%?   _____

4. The list price of 1/2-inch flare nuts is 65¢ each. If the discount is 25%, what do 12 nuts cost, net?   _____

5. Glove compartment light assemblies cost 85¢ each, list. The discount on a purchase of 12 is 25%. What is the net cost of the purchase?   _____

6. Power steering pressure hose is sold by a jobber to a garageman at a discount of 40%. If the list price is 80¢ per foot, what is the garageman's cost per foot?   _____

7. When overhauling an air conditioner compressor, a mechanic used the following items: one gasket, 85¢ each (less 33 1/3%); six piston ball shoes, 65¢ each (less 33 1/3%); one seal kit, $6.60 each (less 25%); one clutch bearing, $7.80 each (less 25%); and seven ounces refrigerant oil, 10¢ per ounce (less 33 1/3%).

   How much is the net cost to the mechanic, if he pays the bill in 10 days, and receives an additional 2% discount for doing so?   _____

8. What is the cost of parts on a job that requires 2 of the 1-inch bolts which cost 90¢ each and 2 nuts that cost 40¢ each if a discount of 33 1/3% is allowed?   _____

9. The list price of the parts used to repair a car is $16.70, of which $12.00 is subject to a 33 1/3% discount from list. What is the net cost of the parts?   _____

10. By purchasing number 12-gage wire in 500-foot rolls, an additional 10% discount is allowed (the discount is then 50%). If the list price is 8¢ per foot, what is the net cost of the roll?   _____

11. The monthly accounts owed by a service station total $467.62. If these accounts are paid on or before the 10th of the succeeding month, they are subject to a 2% discount. What is the total of all accounts after the discount is taken?   _____

Unit 21   PROFIT AND LOSS, COMMISSIONS

BASIC PRINCIPLES OF PROFIT AND LOSS, COMMISSIONS

- Review unit 26 in *Basic Mathematics Simplified* for the principles of percentage as applied to profit and loss, and commissions.

- Apply the principles of profit and loss and commissions to the automotive field by solving the Review Problems which follow.

REVIEW PROBLEMS

1. The total receipts of a repair shop for a certain month are $2,000.00. Of this amount, 40% is paid out as wages, 10% as rent, 5% for heat and 20% to cover all other miscellaneous overhead expenses. Does the shop show a profit? If so, how much, in dollars and cents and in percentage? _____ _____

2. A garageman buys a job lot of 500 feet of number 12-gage wire. He pays 8.5¢ per foot for it. The next day the price of this wire increases 12 1/2%. How much does he save by purchasing it when he does? _____

3. A garageman buys a quantity of different size tires at a sale for $725.45. He also pays $26.30 for freight charges. He sells these tires so that he makes a profit of 33 1/3%, on the cost. How much does he get for the tires? _____

4. A certain make of automobile priced at $1965.75 depreciates 35% in one year. How much money does a purchaser lose in depreciation in one year? _____

5. A certain make of automobile priced at $1875.00 is reduced 23%. What is the sale price after the reduction? _____

6. If a drum of grease containing 54 gallons and weighing 7 pounds per gallon, is subject to a 5% loss through wastage, what is the net loss to the garageman if the grease costs him 7 1/2¢ per pound? _____

7. What is the charge to a customer for flushing out and refilling the rear end of a car if the flushing liquid, of which 2 quarts are used, costs 19¢ per gallon; the refill takes 4 pints at a cost of 17 1/2¢ per pint; the labor charge is 75¢; and the garage receives a 100% profit on the material? _____

8. An automobile costs $1650.00 and is sold at a profit of 25% on the cost price. What is the profit? _____

9. A mechanic receives a commission of 5% on parts he is able to sell customers. He sells $29.00 worth of parts. What is his commission? _____

10. An agent receives $72.50 commission for selling a $1650.00 car. What rate of commission does he get? _____

11. A car sells for $2,210.00 on which a commission of 15% is allowed. What is the amount of commission paid? _____

Unit 22   INTEREST AND TAXES

BASIC PRINCIPLES OF INTEREST AND TAXES

- Study unit 31 in *Basic Mathematics Simplified* for the principles of percentage as applied to interest and taxes.

- Apply the principles of interest and taxes to the automotive field by solving the Review Problems which follow.

REVIEW PROBLEMS

1. How much in interest will $300.00 earn in one year if the interest rate is 3%?   _____

2. A garage owner's bank account averages $3,600.00 for two years at an interest rate of 2 1/2%.   How much interest does this account yield?   _____

3. A man borrows $100.00 from a loan company which charges 3% interest per month on the unpaid balance. If he repays the loan in 20 monthly payments of $5.00 each plus interest —

   a.   How much interest has he paid?   _____

   b.   What percentage of his loan is interest?   _____

4. Some banks make loans at 6% interest discounted. This means the interest is figured and deducted from the amount being borrowed.   For example, if $100.00 is borrowed at 6%, the interest will amount to $6.00. This deducted from the $100.00 and the borrower receives only $94.00, but has to pay $100.00.   He is thus paying $6.00 for a loan of $94.00.

   a.   What is the actual rate of interest in this case?   _____

   b.   Will the rate of interest be the same if $500.00 is borrowed at 6% discount?   _____

   Note: Tax rates are expressed commonly in three ways:

   a.   =   mills per dollar value — 1 mill equals 1/1000 of a dollar or 1/10 cent

   b.   =   dollars per hundred dollars of value

   c.   =   dollars per thousand dollars of value

5. What percentage does a tax rate of 20 mills per dollar equal? That is, the tax is what percentage of the value?   _____

6. What percentage does a tax rate of $3.50 per hundred dollars equal?   _____

7. What percentage does a tax rate of $29.50 per thousand dollars equal?   _____

8. An automobile repair shop owner has a plant with equipment values at $12,000.00. If the tax rate in his community is 25 mills, what is his tax bill?   _____

9. A car is valued at $1,750.00. If the personal property tax rate is $28.00 per thousand, how much is the owner taxed?   _____

Unit 23   PERCENTAGE ERROR AND AVERAGES

BASIC PRINCIPLES OF PERCENTAGE ERROR AND AVERAGES

- Study unit 27, in *Basic Mathematics Simplified* for the principles of averages and estimates.

- Apply the principles of percentage error and averages to the automotive field by solving the Review Problems which follow.

REVIEW PROBLEMS

1. The speedometer of a car shows 50 miles per hour, but actually the speed is 46 miles per hour. What is the percentage of error?   _____

2. If a speed of 35 miles per hour is registered on the speedometer but the true speed is 42 miles per hour, what is the percentage of error?   _____

3. If 1/10 of 1% is the amount of error permitted in the size of structural steel, how much of a variation in depth is permitted on an "I" beam which is 8 inches deep?   _____

   Note: Averages are found by adding all the parts and dividing by the number of parts.

4. What is the average hourly rate if three mechanics in a shop receive respectively $2.05 per hour, $2.12 per hour, and $2.25 per hour?   _____

5. What is the average number of miles traveled per day if on a trip the mileage is as follows: Monday, 328 miles; Tuesday, 461 miles; Wednesday, 395 miles; Thursday, 407 miles?   _____

6. What is the average number of miles per gallon of gasoline if a car travels the distance recorded and uses the fuel indicated below?   _____

Speedometer Reading		No. of Gallons of Gas Purchased
Start	28,352	3 gals. in tank
	28,352	7 gals.
	28,480	10 gals.
	28,590	6.4 gals.
	28,700	8.7 gals.
Finish	28,875	2 gals. in tank

7. In a group of ten students the following marks are received on a test: 2 students, 85%; 4 students, 78%; 3 students, 66%; and 1 student, 92%. What is the class average?   _____

Unit 24   MEASUREMENTS (LINEAR)

BASIC PRINCIPLES OF LINEAR MEASURE

- Study unit 19 in *Basic Mathematics Simplified* for the principles of linear measure.
- Apply the principles of linear measure to the automotive field by solving the Review Problems which follow.

REVIEW PROBLEMS

Note: Give answers to the nearest 1/16 inch where necessary.

1. An automobile frame measures 9 feet 6 5/8 inches. What is the total length in inches? _____

2. From a roll of 3/8-inch tubing 20 feet long, one piece 6 feet 9 3/4 inches is cut. What length piece remains? Express answer in feet and inches. _____

3. Two pieces of copper tubing each measuring 3 feet 8 7/8 inches are cut from a coil 10 feet long. What length remains? Express answer in feet and inches. _____

4. Pieces of ignition wire 2 feet 3 7/16 inches, 6 feet 11 1/4 inches, and 11 feet 9 3/8 inches are cut from a roll which measures 25 feet. How many feet and inches remain? _____

5. In a repair shop, the owner wishes to mark off six repair stalls, each to be 8 feet 5 3/4 inches wide. What is the total distance necessary to accommodate these six stalls? _____

6. A parking lot has a frontage of 250 feet. How many cars can be parked along the front if 7 feet 6 inches is allowed for each car and 12 feet 8 inches is allowed for a roadway in the center? _____

7. Change 25.4 miles to feet and inches. _____

8. Change 8.65 miles to feet and inches. _____

9. Change 6.75 miles to feet and inches. _____

10. Express 5 feet 3 inches entirely in feet. _____

11. Express 2 feet 1 1/2 inches entirely in feet. _____

12. Express 8 feet 10 1/4 inches entirely in feet. _____

13. A mile is equal to 5,280 feet. How many yards are in a mile? _____

14. Change 1,156 inches to yards, feet, and inches. _____

15. Change 2 1/2 miles to yards. _____

16. What part of a mile is 1,000 feet? _____

Unit 25 METRIC MEASUREMENT

BASIC PRINCIPLES OF METRIC MEASUREMENT

- Study unit 23 in *Basic Mathematics Simplified* for the principles of metric measurement.
- Apply the principles of metric measurement to the automotive field by solving the Review Problems which follow.

REVIEW PROBLEMS

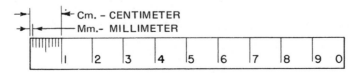

1. How many centimeters are there in one meter? _____

2. How many millimeters are there in one meter? _____

3. How many millimeters are there in 2 1/2 meters? _____

4. How many centimeters are there in 275 millimeters? _____

5. How many millimeters are there in 26 centimeters? _____

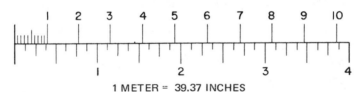

1 METER = 39.37 INCHES

6. Change 6 centimeters to inches. _____

7. Change 37 millimeters to inches. _____

8. Express in inches the diameter of an 18-millimeter spark plug. _____

9. A generator pulley is 4 inches in diameter. What is its diameter in millimeters? _____

10. One size International Standard thread has a diameter of 22 millimeters and a pitch of 2 1/2 millimeters.

    a. What is the diameter in inches? (to the nearest thousandth of an inch) _____

    b. Approximately how many threads per inch are there?

11. How many threads per centimeter does a 1/4-inch — NF screw have? _____

12. In problem 11, what is the diameter of the screw in millimeters? _____

13. What is the inside micrometer setting if the cylinders of a foreign automobile are honed to fit a 150-millimeter piston, allowing .002 clearance? _____

Unit 26   CIRCULAR MEASUREMENT

BASIC PRINCIPLES OF CIRCULAR MEASUREMENT

- Study unit 20 in *Basic Mathematics Simplified* for principles of circular measurements.

- Apply the principles of circular measurements to the automotive field by solving the Review Problems which follow.

REVIEW PROBLEMS

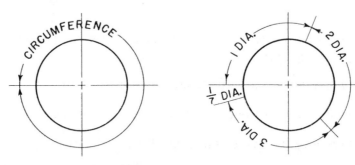

Note: The circumference is the distance around a circle and is equal in length to 3 1/7 (approximately) diameters.

1. If the diameter of a circle is 3 inches, find the circumference.

   _____

2. If the diameter is 4 7/16 inches, find the circumference.

   _____

3. What is the circumference of the fan pulley in the illustration at the right?

   _____

4. What is the circumference of the crankshaft pulley?

   _____

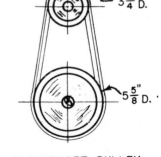

FAN PULLEY

$3\frac{3}{4}''$ D.

$5\frac{5}{8}''$ D.

CRANKSHAFT PULLEY

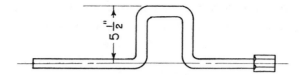

5. How far does the hand travel in one turn of the tire wrench?

   _____

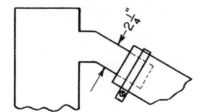

6. How long a clamp strap is necessary to go around the hose connection if the hose wall is 1/8 inch thick?

   _____

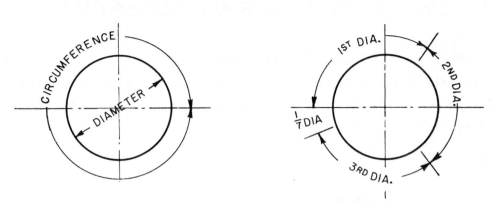

Note: The diameter of a circle equals the circumference divided by 3 1/7 (approximate) or (3.1416).

7. The circumference of a circle is 2 1/16 inches. What is the diameter? _____

8. With a circumference of 5 1/2 inches, what is the diameter of the circle? _____

9. A 6-inch wire is bent into the shape of a circle. What is the diameter of this circle? _____

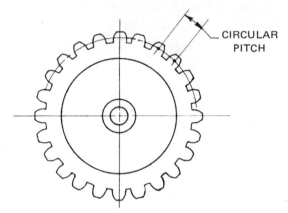

CIRCULAR
PITCH

10. If the pitch circle of the gear is 5 1/4 inches in diameter, and it has 24 teeth, what is the distance (measured on the circumference of pitch circle) between teeth? _____

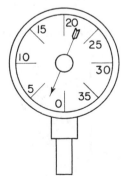

11. A gage 5 inches in diameter has a face which is to be divided into 8 parts. How far is measured on the circumference for these divisions? _____

Unit 27 ANGULAR MEASUREMENT

BASIC PRINCIPLES OF ANGLES

- Review unit 20 in *Basic Mathematics Simplified* for the principles of angles.

- Apply the principles of angles to the automotive field by solving the Review Problems which follow.

REVIEW PROBLEMS

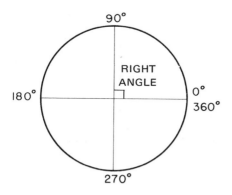

1 circle = 360°

4 right angles = 1 circle

1 right angle = 90°

1 degree (1°) = 60 minutes (60′)

1 minute (1′) = 60 seconds (60″)

1. How many degrees are there in a semicircle? _____

2. How many degrees are there in a quarter of a circle? _____

3. What part of a circle is a 60° angle? _____

4. What part of a circle is a 45° angle? _____

5. What part of a circle is a 30° angle? _____

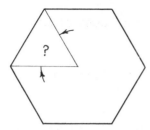   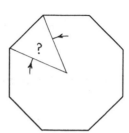

6. What size angle is formed at the center of a circle opposite one of the sides of a hexagon? _____

7. What size angle is formed at the center of a circle opposite one of the sides of an octagon? _____

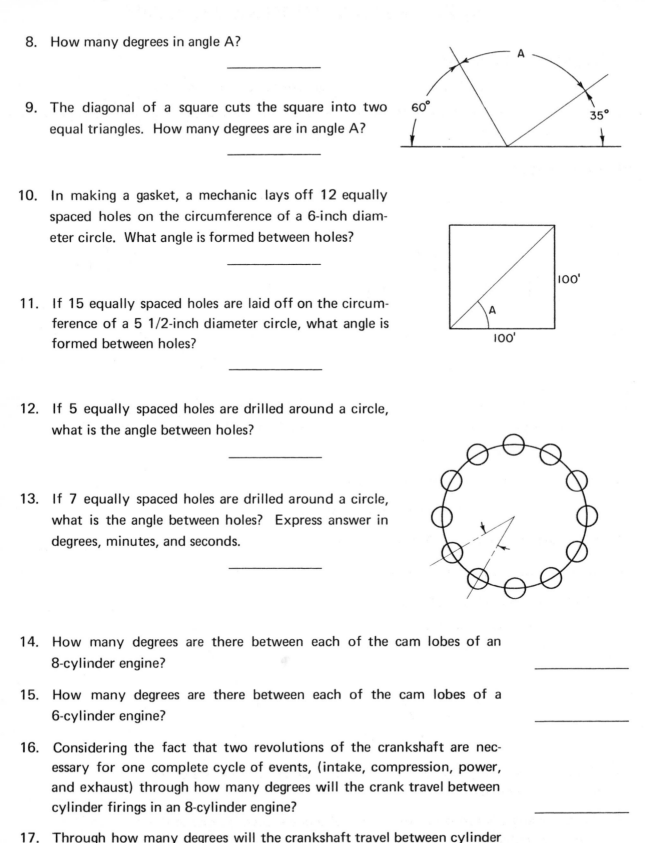

8. How many degrees in angle A?

    _____

9. The diagonal of a square cuts the square into two equal triangles. How many degrees are in angle A?

    _____

10. In making a gasket, a mechanic lays off 12 equally spaced holes on the circumference of a 6-inch diameter circle. What angle is formed between holes?

    _____

11. If 15 equally spaced holes are laid off on the circumference of a 5 1/2-inch diameter circle, what angle is formed between holes?

    _____

12. If 5 equally spaced holes are drilled around a circle, what is the angle between holes?

    _____

13. If 7 equally spaced holes are drilled around a circle, what is the angle between holes? Express answer in degrees, minutes, and seconds.

    _____

14. How many degrees are there between each of the cam lobes of an 8-cylinder engine?

    _____

15. How many degrees are there between each of the cam lobes of a 6-cylinder engine?

    _____

16. Considering the fact that two revolutions of the crankshaft are necessary for one complete cycle of events, (intake, compression, power, and exhaust) through how many degrees will the crank travel between cylinder firings in an 8-cylinder engine?

    _____

17. Through how many degrees will the crankshaft travel between cylinder firings in a 6-cylinder engine?

    _____

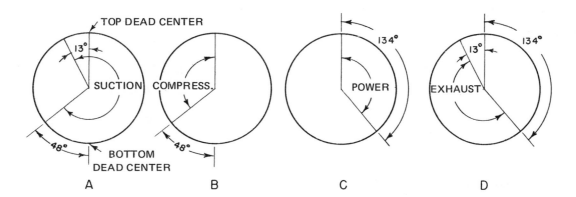

18. If the intake valve opens when the crank is 13 degrees ahead of top dead center and closes 48 degrees after bottom dead center, through how many degrees does the crank move on the suction stroke? See A.

_____

19. All valves are closed from 48 degrees past bottom dead center to exact top dead center. Through how many degrees does the crank travel during the compression stroke? See B.

_____

20. If the crank travels through 134 degrees on the power stroke, how many degrees before bottom dead center does the exhaust valve open? See C.

_____

21. If the exhaust valve opens at the end of the power stroke and remains open until crank is 13 degrees ahead of top dead center, through how many degrees does the crank travel during the exhaust period? See D.

_____

22. What percentage of the entire cycle of strokes is the power stroke? Use 134-degree power stroke.

_____

23. A certain engine is timed when the inlet valve opens (8 degrees past top dead center) and there is no mark on the flywheel to indicate this position. What distance on the circumference of the 18-inch diameter flywheel is measured from the line of top dead center to get the proper position of crank?

_____

Change degrees on the rim of the flywheel to inches in the following problems:

24. How many inches is 5 degrees on a 16-inch diameter flywheel?

_____

25. How many inches is 20 degrees on a 21-inch diameter flywheel?

_____

26. How many inches is 40 degrees on a 14 1/2-inch diameter flywheel?

_____

Unit 28   UNITS OF AREA AND VOLUME MEASURE

BASIC PRINCIPLES OF AREA AND VOLUME

- Study units 21 and 22 in *Basic Mathematics Simplified* for the principles of area and volume.

- Apply the principles of area and volume to the automotive field by solving the Review Problems which follow.

REVIEW PROBLEMS

1. How many square feet are there in a parking area 200 feet x 150 feet? _____

2. What part of an acre is this lot? (An acre contains 43,560 square feet.) _____

3. Cork gasket material is purchased by the square foot. If the roll is 30 inches wide, what is the length in feet in an order of 25 square feet? _____

4. Allowing a piece 2 1/2 feet long and 14 inches wide for a head gasket, how many gaskets can be cut out of the roll in problem 3? _____

5. How many square inches are there in one of the head gaskets in problem 4? _____

6. Fiberglass costs $2.15 per square foot. What is the cost of a piece 3 feet x 42 inches? _____

7. A mechanic relines a truck body with flat stock. The floor measures 10 feet x 8 feet, the sides are 10 feet x 6 feet and the front measures 8 feet x 6 feet. What is the total area covered? _____

8. If a space 12 feet x 8 feet is allowed for 1 car in a storage garage with an area of 12,000 square feet, how many cars can be parked? _____

9. How many square inches of active material are there in a 6-cell storage battery with 8 positive plates per cell? Each plate measures 5 1/2 inches x 6 1/4 inches. Both sides of the plates are active. _____

10. The owner of a 40 x 30-foot garage charges $.25 per square foot per month rental. What is the rent per month? _____

11. A mechanic wishes to build a garage. He figures the following spaces are needed: grease rack 20 feet x 10 feet, motor repair for 3 cars 20 feet x 30 feet, benches 30 feet x 2 feet, wash rack 20 feet x 10 feet, and storage 13 feet x 10 feet. What is the cost at $9.25 per square foot? _____

Note: Specific gravity refers to the weight of a substance compared to an equal quantity of water. For example, lead has a specific gravity of approximately 8 which means lead is 8 times as heavy as an equal volume of water.

The values listed will be helpful in solving the problems which follow:

Water	= 1.000 specific gravity
Sulphuric Acid	= 1.835 specific gravity
Alcohol	= .816 specific gravity
Gasoline	= .728 specific gravity

1 cubic foot	= 1,728 cubic inches
1 U.S. Gallon	= 231 cubic inches
1 cubic foot of water	= 62.5 pounds
1 U.S. Gallon of water	= 8.333 pounds

12. What is the weight of a gallon of gasoline?   _____

13. How many pints does a pound of gasoline contain?   _____

14. What is the weight of the contents of a 50-gallon drum of alcohol?   _____

15. Sulphuric acid for storage batteries is sometimes shipped in 200-pound carboys (200 pounds of liquid). If the specific gravity is 1.835, how many gallons will this carboy hold?   _____

16. The legal load limit of a 1-ton delivery truck, in a certain locality is 2,000 pounds. A 550-gallon tank weighing 185 pounds is mounted on a 1-ton truck. The tank is filled with gasoline. By how many pounds does the load exceed the legal limit?   _____

17. How many gallons are there in a cubic foot of water?   _____

18. How many gallons does a cubic foot of gasoline contain?   _____

19. An Imperial gallon such as is used in Canada and Great Britain contains 277.274 cubic inches. How many pints does this equal? Give answer to 3 decimal places.   _____

20. If gasoline is selling in the United States for $.24 a gallon, what, at the same rate, does an Imperial gallon cost?   _____

21. How many United States quarts equal ten Imperial gallons?   _____

22. How many Imperial gallons can a 10-gallon (U.S.) tank hold without overflowing?   _____

23. A dump truck is carrying 2 cubic yards of loam. How heavy is the load if the weight of loam per cubic foot is 125 pounds?   _____

Unit 29 TIME AND MONEY CALCULATIONS

BASIC PRINCIPLES OF TIME AND SPEED

- Study unit 29 in *Basic Mathematics Simplified* for the principles of time and speed.

- Apply the principles of time and speed to the automotive field by solving the Review Problems which follow.

REVIEW PROBLEMS

1. A mechanic's time card shows he started on a valve grinding job at 8:27 a.m. and finished at 3:10 p.m. Allowing an hour for lunch, how much does he make at $1.65 per hour? _____

2. The flat rate price for the labor on a job is $39.00. The job takes 6 hours. What are the average hourly earnings of the mechanic if he receives 50% of flat rate? _____

3. If time allowance for a certain assembly job is 20 minutes, how many jobs is this worker expected to do in an 8-hour day? _____

4. If a mechanic is paid $1.75 per hour, how long should he take to complete a job where the allowance for labor is $21.15? Express answer in hours and any remainder in minutes. _____

5. On the basis of an 8-hour working day, how many days and hours are required to complete a job taking 102 hours? _____

6. With an 8-hour day and a 40-hour week, how many weeks, days and hours are equal to 210 hours? _____

7. How many minutes are equal to .6 hour? _____

8. If a worker is 23 minutes late, how many tenths of an hour are deducted from his time? _____

9. If 30 minutes are required to travel 10 miles, what is the average rate of speed in miles per hour? _____

10. If 45 miles are traveled in 50 minutes, what is the average rate of speed in miles per hour? _____

11. If 80 miles are traveled in one hour and 45 minutes, what is the average rate of speed in miles per hour? _____

12. If 150 miles are traveled in 4.6 hours, what is the average rate of speed in miles per hour? _____

13. How many miles per minute does an airplane travel, at a speed of 350 miles per hour?

    _____

14. How many feet per second equal a speed of 60 miles per hour?

    Note: a nautical mile = 1.152 land miles.

    _____

15. A boat has a speed of 28 knots (nautical miles per hour). Express this speed in miles per hour.

    _____

16. What is the speed in miles per hour of a ship with a top speed of 32 knots?

    _____

17. How many knots equal a land speed of 50 miles per hour?

    _____

18. How many knots does a boat travel to equal a land speed of 60 miles per hour?

    Note: Revolutions per minute is expressed as r.p.m.

    _____

19. A V-8 engine is turning over at 3,600 r.p.m. How many times will the points open in 1 minute?

    _____

    Note: The engine takes 2 revolutions to every 1 revolution of the distributor.

20. What is the average speed of a piston in feet per minute if the engine is running 3,400 r.p.m. and has a 4-inch stroke?

    _____

21. The breaker points in the distributor of a 4-cylinder engine open 15 times per second. What is the number of revolutions per minute for the flywheel?

    _____

Unit 30   SPEED RATIOS

BASIC PRINCIPLES OF SPEED RATIOS

- Study unit 51 in *Basic Mathematics Simplified* for the principles of ratio.

- Apply the principles of ratio and proportion to the automotive field by solving the Review Problems in speed ratios which follow.

REVIEW PROBLEMS

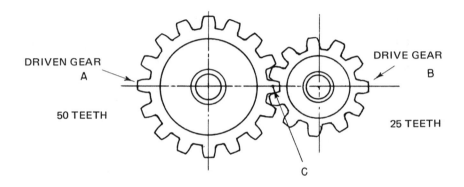

Note: In this case, if gear A makes one turn, 50 teeth pass point C. Since the teeth in gear A are in mesh with the teeth in gear B the same number of teeth on gear B must pass point C. In order for 50 teeth on gear B to pass point C, gear B must make 2 turns. Therefore, gear B is turning twice as fast as gear A and the speed ratio of gear B to A would be 2:1. Speed ratios are usually driver to driven.

1. Gear A has 60 teeth and gear B has 20 teeth.

   a. What is the ratio of teeth on A to teeth on B?

   b. What is the speed ratio of A to B?

2. Gear A has 75 teeth and gear B has 10 teeth.

   a. What is the ratio of teeth A to B?

   b. What is the speed ratio?

3. If a speed ratio of 3.5:1 is desired, and the small gear has 20 teeth, how many teeth should the larger gear have?

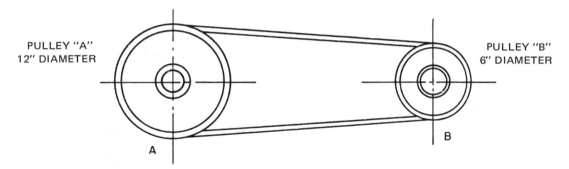

PULLEY "A"
12" DIAMETER

PULLEY "B"
6" DIAMETER

A

B

Note: Pulley A is twice as large as pulley B. In one turn of pulley A, a length of belt equal to its circumference will move. In order for the same length of belt to cause motion in pulley B, pulley B must make 2 turns (assuming no slippage.)

_____

4.   Pulley A is 35 inches in diameter and pulley B is 7 inches in diameter.

   a.   What is the ratio of the size A to B?   _____

   b.   What is the speed ratio of A to B?   _____

5.   If pulley A = 16 inches and B = 3 inches, what is speed ratio of A to B?   _____

6.   If a speed ratio of 5:3 is desirable, what large size pulley is necessary if   _____
     the small pulley is a 15-inch pulley?

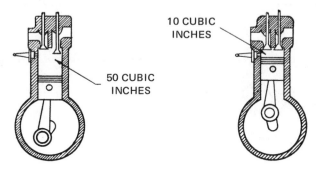

10 CUBIC
INCHES

50 CUBIC
INCHES

Note: Compression ratio is a comparison between the amount of space (cubic inches) in the cylinder when the piston is at the bottom of the stroke, and the space when the piston is at the top of the stroke. If there is five times as much space when the piston is at the top of the stroke, the compression ratio is 5:1.

7.   What is the compression ratio if there are 33 cubic inches of space when   _____
     the piston is at the bottom of the stroke and only 5 cubic inches when
     the piston is at the top of the stroke?

8.   What is the compression ratio if there are 43 cubic inches of space when   _____
     the piston is at the bottom of the stroke and only 8 cubic inches when
     the piston is at the top of the stroke?

9. What is the compression ratio if 36.5 cubic inches of space exist when the piston is at the bottom of the stroke and only 4.7 cubic inches of space exist when the piston is at the top of the stroke?   _____

    Note: The compression ratio can be determined for an L-head engine as follows:

    a. Put piston on dead center.

    b. Weigh a 2-quart container of light machine oil carefully.

    c. Pour oil through spark plug hole until it is level with bottom of the hole.

    d. Weigh container and oil to determine amount used to fill combustion space.

    e. Put piston on bottom dead center making sure exhaust valve is closed by backing off on tappet adjusting screw.

    f. Pour in oil to fill the cylinder space completely.

    g. Weigh container and oil to find amount used for cylinder space.

10. Determine the compression ratio if the weights recorded in the test outlined above are for (b) 58 ounces, (d) 50 ounces, and (g) 14 ounces.   _____

    Note: Transmission ratio refers to the number of times the speed is reduced by the transmission. A transmission ratio of 5:1 means the speed is reduced 5 times by the transmission or that the r.p.m. of the crankshaft is 5 times the r.p.m. of the drive shaft.

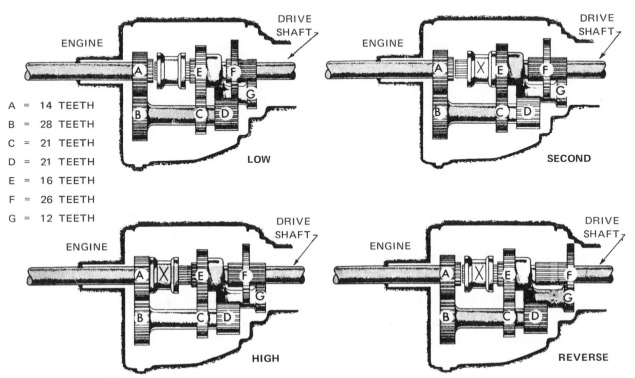

A = 14 TEETH
B = 28 TEETH
C = 21 TEETH
D = 21 TEETH
E = 16 TEETH
F = 26 TEETH
G = 12 TEETH

LOW   SECOND   HIGH   REVERSE

11. In low speed (1st), gears A, B, E, and F are in mesh. What is the transmission ratio in low speed?   _____

12. In intermediate speed (2nd), gears A, B, C, and D are in mesh. What is the transmission ratio in intermediate speed? _____

13. In high speed the splines on gear D mesh with teeth inside gear A. This gives a direct drive. What is the transmission ratio in high speed? _____

14. In reverse, gears A, B, G, and F are in mesh. What is the transmission ratio? The reverse idler changes direction of rotation but does not affect the speed. _____

   Note: Rear axle ratios refer to the number of times the speed is reduced by the ring gear and pinion. A rear axle ratio of 5:1 means that the r.p.m. of the drive shaft is 5 times as great as the r.p.m. of the rear axle.

15. If the pinion has 16 teeth and the ring gear has 64 teeth, what is rear axle ratio? _____

16. If the pinion has 14 teeth and the ring gear has 63 teeth, what is rear axle ratio? _____

17. If the pinion has 19 teeth and the ring gear has 90 teeth, what is rear axle ratio? _____

   Note: Both the transmission and differential serve to reduce the original r.p.m. of the crankshaft. Both are considered to get a measure of the total gear reduction. For example, 4 transmission ratio x 5 rear axle ratio = 20 total gear reduction. This means the crankshaft turns 20 times while the rear axle turns once.

18. In low speed the transmission ratio of a car is 3.5:1 and the rear axle ratio is 4.7:1. What is the total gear reduction? _____

19. In the same car as in problem 18, the second speed transmission ratio is 1.8:1. What is the total gear reduction? _____

20. What is the total gear reduction in direct-drive position if the pinion gear has 15 teeth and the ring gear has 65 teeth? _____

Unit 31   PROPORTION

BASIC PRINCIPLES OF PROPORTION

- Review unit 52 in *Basic Mathematics Simplified* for the principles of proportion.

- Apply the principles of proportion to the automotive field by solving the Review Problems which follow.

REVIEW PROBLEMS

1. A gear with 40 teeth turning 200 r.p.m. is in mesh with a gear of 10 teeth. Find the r.p.m. of the small gear.   _____

2. A gear of 15 teeth turning 150 r.p.m. is driving a gear of 25 teeth. Find the r.p.m. of the driven gear.   _____

3. A 28-tooth gear running 320 r.p.m. drives another gear at 128 r.p.m. How many teeth does the drive gear have?   _____

4. Two gears have a speed ratio of 3.6:1. If the larger gear has 72 teeth, how many teeth does the smaller gear have?   _____

5. Two shafts 12 inches apart are connected by gears so that the speed ratio is 2:1. What is the pitch diameter of the gears which are used?   _____

6. Two chain-driven timing gear sprockets have teeth as follows: smaller sprocket, 12 teeth, r.p.m. 1800; larger sprocket, 21 teeth. Find the r.p.m. of the larger sprocket.   _____

7. With a transmission ratio of 3.8:1, what is the r.p.m. of the drive shaft if the crankshaft speed is 1520 r.p.m.?   _____

8. With a rear axle ratio of 5.2:1, what is the r.p.m. of the rear axle if the drive shaft is turning 900 r.p.m.?   _____

9. If the rear axle ratio is 4.5:1 and the pinion has 16 teeth, how many teeth does the ring gear have?   _____

10. With a total gear reduction of 10.4:1, what is the r.p.m. of the crankshaft if the rear wheels are turning 150 r.p.m.?   _____

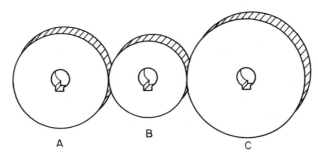

11. Gear A has 32 teeth; gear B (idler) has 16 teeth; gear C has 48 teeth. What is the speed of C if A turns 300 r.p.m.? _____

12. In problem 11, find speed of gear C if it meshes with A without idler. _____

13. Does the idler cause any change in speed? _____

14. What is the direction of rotation of gear C in problem 11 if gear A rotates clockwise? _____

15. What is the direction of rotation of gear C in problem 12 if gear A rotates clockwise? _____

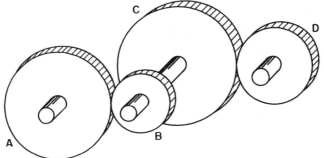

16. Gear A = 30 teeth, gear B = 15 teeth, gear C = 40 teeth, gear D = 20 teeth. The r.p.m. of gear A = 300; what is the r.p.m. of gear C? _____

17. Using the same size gears as in problem 16, assume gear D is the driving gear and is turning 600 r.p.m. What is the r.p.m. of gear A? _____

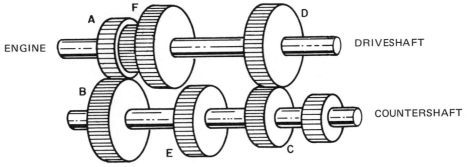

18. In the transmission, gear A has 14 teeth; gear B has 28 teeth; gear C has 18 teeth; gear D has 24 teeth. The crankshaft is turning 1,800 r.p.m. What is the r.p.m. of the drive shaft? _____

19. In second speed in this transmission, gear E, 27 teeth, meshes with gear F, 25 teeth. What is the r.p.m. of the drive shaft if the crankshaft is still turning 1,800 r.p.m.? _____

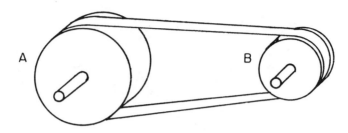

20. Pulley A is 18 inches; pulley B is 4 inches; r.p.m. of A is 500; find the r.p.m. of B. _____

21. Find the r.p.m. of the generator pulley if the crankshaft turns 1,200 r.p.m. _____

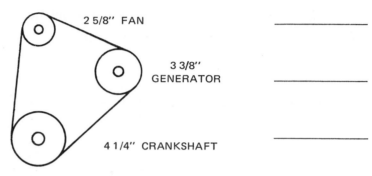

2 5/8″ FAN

3 3/8″ GENERATOR

4 1/4″ CRANKSHAFT

22. Find the r.p.m. of the fan pulley if the crankshaft turns 1,200 r.p.m. _____

23. What diameter pulley would turn 1,500 r.p.m. if it were being driven by a 3-inch pulley rotating 350 r.p.m.? _____

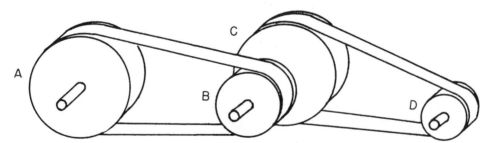

24. Pulley A is 10 inches; pulley B is 2 1/4 inches; pulley C is 8 3/4 inches; D is 3 1/2 inches; r.p.m. of A is 800. Find the r.p.m. of D. _____

25. A is 12 inches; B is 5 inches; C is 15 inches; r.p.m. of A is 1,000; r.p.m. of D is 250; find the diameter of pulley D. _____

Note: Corresponding sides of similar triangles (triangles which have the same angles) are in proportion. That is,

$$\frac{a}{A} = \frac{b}{B}, \quad \frac{a}{A} = \frac{c}{C}, \quad \frac{b}{B} = \frac{c}{C} \qquad OR \qquad \begin{aligned} a:A &= b:B \\ a:A &= c:C \\ b:B &= c:C \end{aligned}$$

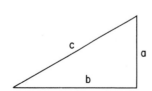

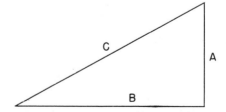

26. a = 4   b = 7   B = 21   Find A.   _____

27. A = 10   B = 25   a = 6   Find b.   _____

28. B = 8   C = 20   c = 8   Find b.   _____

29. The state automobile inspection permits headlights set at an angle pro-   _____
vided the drop in the light beam is not greater than 2 inches for each
25 feet measured horizontally. How far ahead of the car is the roadway
illuminated if the headlight is 28 inches above the ground and the rate
of drop is 2 inches per 25 feet?

30. If headlights, 30 inches above the road, are tilted so that the drop in   _____
light beam measured with a tester is 4 inches per 25 feet, how far ahead
of the car does the light beam hit the road?

31. If headlights which are 2 feet above the road illuminate the roadway   _____
500 feet ahead of the car, what rate of drop does the light beam have?
Express answer in inches per 25 feet.

32. If the rate of drop in light beam is 1 inch per 25 feet, how high should   _____
the headlights be mounted to illuminate the roadway 250 yards ahead
of the car?

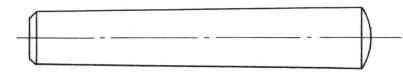

STANDARD TAPER PIN

Note: Taper is the difference in diameter between the two ends.

33. Standard taper pins all have a taper equal to 1/4 inch per foot. What is   _____
the difference in diameter between the two ends if a taper pin is 4
inches long?

34. If the large end of a standard taper pin #000 measures .125 inch, what   _____
should the small end measure if the pin is 1 inch long?

35. If the small end of a #3 standard taper pin measures .177 inch, what   _____
does the large end measure if the pin is 2 inches long?

36. What is the length of a standard taper pin if the large end measures   _____
.375 inch and the small end measures .3125 inch?

37. If a car travels 15 miles per hour (m.p.h.) when the crankshaft speed is   _____
1,000 r.p.m., how fast is the car going when the crankshaft speed is
3,200 r.p.m.?

38. If the speed of a car is 20 m.p.h. when the crankshaft speed is 2,000 r.p.m., how fast is the crankshaft turning when the speed of the car is 50 m.p.h.?   _____

39. If the top speed of a crankshaft in a car is 4,200 r.p.m. when the car is traveling 75 m.p.h., how fast is the car going when the crankshaft speed is 1,800 r.p.m.?   _____

    Note: 60 miles per hour = 88 feet per second or 1 mile per minute.

40. How many feet per second does a car travel at a speed of 15 m.p.h.?   _____

41. Express in feet per second the speed of 45 m.p.h.   _____

42. Express in feet per second the speed of 25 m.p.h.   _____

43. Express in feet per second the speed of 40 m.p.h.   _____

44. An airplane travels at a speed of 4 miles per minute. Express this speed in m.p.h.   _____

45. A track star can race at a speed of 33 feet per second. Express this speed in m.p.h.   _____

46. When a speedometer is being checked, a car is driven at a uniform speed of 45 miles per hour (speedometer) along the entire length of a measured mile. The time actually taken to travel the mile is 1 minute and 20 seconds.

    a.   Is this the true speed?   _____

    b.   Is the speedometer fast, slow, or correct?   _____

47. Over the same measured mile, a uniform speedometer speed of 35 m.p.h. is kept. The time required is 1 1/2 minutes for the mile.

    a.   Is the speedometer in error?   _____

    b.   Is the speedometer fast, slow, or correct?   _____

48. How much longer does it take to travel 10 miles at 30 miles per hour than at 50 miles per hour?   _____

49. If 10 miles can be traveled in 15 minutes, how long does it take to travel 30 miles at the same average rate of speed?   _____

50. If 48 miles are traveled in 1 hour and 15 minutes, at the same average rate of speed, what distance is traveled in 4 hours and 45 minutes?   _____

51. A time trial for a racing car shows that on a 3/4-mile track one lap is traveled in 38 seconds. At this rate, what time is made in a 100-mile race?   _____

 ECTION 7 — **POWERS AND ROOTS**

Unit 32   POWERS

BASIC PRINCIPLES OF POWERS

- Study unit 55 in *Basic Mathematics Simplified* for the concept of exponents.
- Apply the principles of powers to the automotive field by solving the Review Problems which follow.

REVIEW PROBLEMS

Raise the following expressions to the power indicated.

1. 7^2 _____

2. 8^2 _____

3. 9^2 _____

4. 10^2 _____

5. 11^2 _____

6. 15^2 _____

7. 25^2 _____

8. 30^2 _____

9. 35^2 _____

10. 50^2 _____

Unit 33   ROOTS

BASIC PRINCIPLES OF ROOTS

- Study unit 59 in *Basic Mathematics Simplified* for the principles of roots.

- Apply the principles of roots to the automotive field by solving the Review Problems which follow.

REVIEW PROBLEMS

Solve the following expressions and carry the results out to two places.

1. $\sqrt{81}$ _____

2. $\sqrt{100}$ _____

3. $\sqrt{169}$ _____

4. $\sqrt{361}$ _____

5. $\sqrt{529}$ _____

6. $\sqrt{743}$ _____

7. $\sqrt{892}$ _____

8. $\sqrt{1235}$ _____

9. $\sqrt{1692}$ _____

10. $\sqrt{2000}$ _____

SECTION 8 — FORMULAS

Unit 34   FORMULAS FOR CIRCULAR MEASUREMENTS AND OHM'S LAW

BASIC FORMULAS FOR CIRCULAR MEASUREMENTS AND OHM'S LAW

- Study units 63 and 65 in *Basic Mathematics Simplified* for the concept of formulas as applied to circular measurement and ohm's law.

- Apply the principles of formulas for circular measurements and ohm's law to the automotive field by solving the Review Problems which follow.

REVIEW PROBLEMS

Note: To find voltage, amperage, or resistance in electrical circuits —
E = voltage, I = amperes, R = resistance (ohms).

$$\text{Formula} \quad I = \frac{E}{R}$$

1. The lighting system of an automobile draws 5 1/2 amperes at a battery   _____
    voltage of 11 3/4. Find the resistance of the lighting system.

2. With a 12-volt battery, what is the resistance of the starting motor if   _____
    250 amperes are flowing during starting?

3. If the blower motor in a car heater has a resistance of 9 ohms, what   _____
    current will flow from the 12-volt battery?

4. An automobile horn requires only .4 amperes from a 12-volt battery.   _____
    What is its resistance?

    Note: To find the circumference of a circle —

    C = circumference, D = diameter, and R = radius

    Formula C = πD   OR   C = 2πR

5. If the diameter of a circle is 12 inches, what is the circumference? What   _____
    is the radius?   _____

6. If the circumference of a circle is 50 inches, what does the diameter   _____
    equal in inches? What does the radius equal?   _____

7. If the radius of a circle is 10 inches, what is the circumference?   _____
    What is the diameter?   _____

Note: The need for a differential which allows each rear wheel to turn independently is easily understood when we realize that in turning corners, one wheel must turn at a different rate of speed from the other. The following problems involve figuring this difference in speed and distance traveled by rear wheels when turning corners.

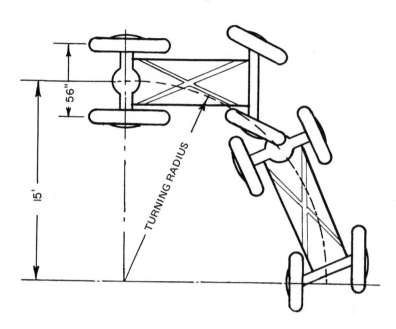

8. With a turning radius of 15 feet (measured from the center of the car to the pivot point), how many feet further would one rear wheel travel than the other in making a 90-degree turn? The standard track or tread equals 56 inches.

9. If a 6.50 x 15-inch tire is used on the rear wheel, how many more turns will one rear wheel make than the other if the conditions are the same as in problem 8?

10. How wide should a road be to permit a U-turn if the smallest turning radius is 13 feet?

11. In order to make a U-turn with a radius of 15 feet, how many feet will one wheel travel further than another?

12. In problem 9, how many more turns will one rear wheel make if 6.50 x 14-inch tires are used on a car?

Note: The area of a circle can be found by using two different formulas both of which give the same result. Since the diameter is more frequently the given dimension, formula #1 is recommended.

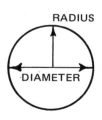

Formula #1   Area = πR^2

Formula #2   Area = $\dfrac{3.1416\,d^2}{4}$ = $.7854\,d^2$

13. Find the area of a circle when the diameter is 6 inches. (Give answer to to nearest thousandth.) _____

14. Find the area of a circle when the diameter is .050 inch. (Give answer to the nearest thousandth.) _____

15. Find the area of a circle when the diameter is 1/4 inch. (Give answer to the nearest thousandth.) _____

16. Find the area of a circle when the radius is 3 5/8 inches. (Give answer to the nearest thousandth.) _____

Note: If the area is known, the diameter can be found by transposing the formula used in the previous problems.

Formula #2 $a = .7854\,d^2$ $\dfrac{a}{.7854} = d^2$ $\sqrt{\dfrac{a}{.7854}} = d$

Formula #1 $a = \pi r^2$ $\dfrac{a}{\pi} = r^2$ $\sqrt{\dfrac{a}{\pi}} = r$

17. Find the diameter of a piston whose area is 50 square inches. _____

18. Find the diameter of an oil drum if the area measures 12.75 square feet. _____

19. What diameter valve is necessary to close an intake port whose area equals 8 3/4 square inches. _____

20. To what radius should dividers be set to lay out a circle having an area of 7/8 square inch? _____

Unit 35   FORMULAS FOR EFFICIENCY

BASIC FORMULAS FOR EFFICIENCY

- Study unit 66 in *Basic Mathematics Simplified* for the principles of formulas for efficiency.
- Apply the formulas for efficiency to the automotive field by solving the Review Problems which follow.

REVIEW PROBLEMS

Note: Both mechanical and thermal efficiency may be found by the use of the following formula. Efficiency is always expressed as a percentage.

$$\text{Efficiency} = \frac{\text{output}}{\text{input}}$$

$$\text{Mechanical efficiency} = \frac{\text{output (foot/pounds of work obtained)}}{\text{input (foot/pounds of work supplied)}}$$

In automobiles:

$$\text{Mech. Eff.} = \frac{\text{brake horsepower}}{\text{indicated horsepower}} = \frac{\text{power delivered to driving wheels}}{\text{power delivered to piston by burning gas}}$$

1. If 100 horsepower is developed by the gasoline but only 90 horsepower is available for actual work, what is the mechanical efficiency? _____

2. In low gear, due to the friction of transmission gears, the horsepower useful in problem 1 is reduced to 83. What is the mechanical efficiency in this case? _____

3. If 65 horsepower is developed but only 50 horsepower is delivered at the driving wheels, what is the mechanical efficiency? _____

$$\text{Efficiency (thermal)} = \frac{\text{output (heat transformed into useful work)}}{\text{input (heat supplied)}}$$

Note: Due to heat escaping by radiation and out the exhaust pipe, the thermal efficiency is necessarily low.

4. If 19,000 British thermal units (Btu.) are changed into useful work but 35,000 Btu. are supplied, what is the thermal efficiency? _____

5. What is the thermal efficiency if out of 50,000 Btu. supplied only 12,000 Btu. are actually used in doing work? _____

6. One gallon of gasoline is used in pulling a load 10 miles. The force necessary to pull the load is 500 pounds. What thermal efficiency does this represent? _____

> 1 gallon of gasoline = 125,000 Btu.
> 1 Btu. = 778 foot/pounds of work

Unit 36   TEMPERATURE

BASIC PRINCIPLES OF TEMPERATURE

- • Review unit 63 in *Basic Mathematics Simplified* for the principles of temperature as applied to formulas.

- • Apply the principles of temperature to the automotive field by solving the Review Problems which follow.

REVIEW PROBLEMS

Note: Two different scales are used in measuring temperatures and the automobile mechanic should be familiar with the process of changing one to the other. These scales are called Fahrenheit and Centigrade.

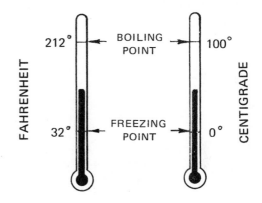

C = 5/9 (F-32) or F = (9/5 x C) + 32

C = temperature in degree centigrade

F = temperature in degrees fahrenheit

1. Wherever heat causes a change in material such as viscosity of oils or specific gravity of liquids, values must be standardized at a definite temperature   This temperature is usually room temperature, 68° fahrenheit. What is the centigrade reading equal to this?   _____

2. Alcohol boils at 179-degrees fahrenheit. What is the centigrade reading equal to this?   _____

Change the melting point temperatures as follows:

Problem	Material	Fahrenheit (in degrees)	Centigrade (in degrees)
3	Cast iron	?	1260
4	Aluminum	1200	?
5	Lead	?	327
6	Copper	1940	?
7	Chromium	2740	?

Unit 37 HORSEPOWER

BASIC PRINCIPLES OF HORSEPOWER

- Study unit 43 in *Basic Mathematics Simplified* for the concept of equations as applied to horsepower formulas.

- Apply the principles of horsepower to the automotive field by solving the Review Problems which follow.

REVIEW PROBLEMS

Note: The following formula can be used for finding the horsepower of any type engine, gasoline, steam, diesel, or compressed air.

$$H.P. = \frac{PLAN}{33,000}$$

P = average pressure (pounds per square inch)

L = length of stroke (feet)

A = area of piston (square inches)

N = number of power strokes per minute

1. Find the horsepower of an automobile engine with a bore of 3.5000 inches, stroke of 2 3/4 inches, average pressure of 125 pounds per square inch and 3,000 power strokes per minute. _____

2. In a 4-cylinder engine, how many power strokes per minute are there if the crankshaft r.p.m. is 2,800? _____

3. In a 6-cylinder engine, how many power strokes per minute are there if the crankshaft r.p.m. is 1,500? _____

4. Find the horsepower in an 8-cylinder engine with a crankshaft speed of 1,500 r.p.m., bore of 2.750 inches, stroke of 4 inches, and average pressure of 100 pounds per square inch. _____

5. What effect does doubling the speed of the crankshaft have on the horsepower? _____

Note: A formula used by manufacturers and for purposes of taxation is called the S.A.E. horsepower formula. This formula does not accurately determine the power but is used simply as a rating.

$$H.P. = \frac{D^2 N}{2.5}$$

D^2 = cylinder bore squared

N = number of cylinders

6. If a 6-cylinder car has a bore of 2.875 inches, what is the horsepower rating? _____

7. What is the horsepower of an 8-cylinder engine with a bore of 3.25 inches? _____

8. How many cylinders are there in a car if the horsepower rating is 21.6 and the bore is 3 inches? _____

Unit 38 CYLINDRICAL VOLUME

BASIC PRINCIPLES OF CYLINDRICAL VOLUME

- Review unit 22 in *Basic Mathematics Simplified* for the principles of volume measure.
- Apply the principles of volume measure to the automotive field by solving the Review Problems which follow.

REVIEW PROBLEMS

Note: The capacity in gallons of cylindrical tanks can be found readily by the use of the following formula.

$$C = \frac{.7854\ D^2\ L}{231}$$

C = capacity in gallons

D = diameter of tank in inches

L = length of tank in inches

231 cubic inches = 1 gallon

1. If the cylindrical gasoline tank in an automobile is 10 inches in diameter and 30 inches long, how many gallons will the tank hold? _____

2. A storage tank for a filling station measures 8 feet long and 4 feet in diameter. What is the capacity of the tank in gallons? _____

3. A drum of alcohol measures 4 feet high and 25 inches in diameter. Is this a 25, 50, 100, 200, or 500-gallon drum? _____

4. If it is necessary to get a 50-gallon tank in a space 3 feet long, what diameter must it be made? _____

5. What is the length of a cylindrical tank 25 inches in diameter which holds 500 gallons? _____

Note: Total piston displacement can be found by the use of the following formula. _____

P.D. = $.7854\ D^2\ LN$ 　　D = diameter of bore of cylinder

L = length of stroke (inches)

N = number of cylinders

P.D. = piston displacement (cubic inches)

6. Find the total piston displacement for a 6-cylinder engine with a 3.750-inch bore and a 3 3/4-inch stroke. _____

7. What is the total piston displacement of an 8-cylinder engine with a 3 1/2-inch diameter and a 4 3/8-inch stroke? _____

8. Find the number of cylinders in an engine with a piston diameter of 3 1/4 inches, a 4 7/8-inch stroke, and piston displacement of 323.5 cubic inches. _____

9. Find the piston diameter of a 6-cylinder engine with piston displacement of 235.5 cubic inches and 3 15/16-inch stroke. _____

Unit 39   USE OF GRAPHS

BASIC PRINCIPLES OF GRAPHS

- Study units 33, 34, and 35 in *Basic Mathematics Simplified* for the principles of bar, line, and circle graphs.

- Apply the principles of bar, line, and circle graphs to the automotive field by solving the Review Problems which follow.

REVIEW PROBLEMS

1. Make a line graph to show the change in the specific gravity of a   _____
    solution in an automobile battery with the decrease of voltage of one
    cell during a starting test as given by the table below:

Voltage	Specific Gravity
2.00	1.300
1.99	1.295
1.96	1.285
1.93	1.280
1.88	1.275
1.84	1.270
1.80	1.265
1.72	1.253
1.52	1.250

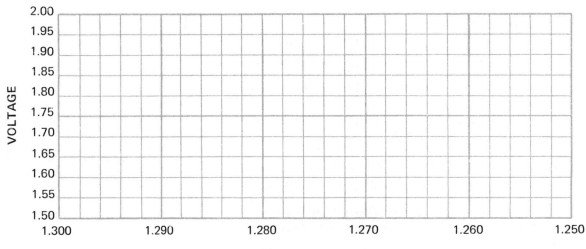

2. What is the specific gravity of the solution in an automobile battery if   _____
    the voltage is 1.90?

3. Plot a line graph of the output of a certain parts manufacturer for his first two years. Use solid line (or blue pencil) for his first year and a dotted line (or red pencil) for his second year.

Month	Year One Output	Year Two Output
Jan.	560	618
Feb.	617	315
March	324	676
April	784	833
May	963	1175
June	782	1005
July	932	931
August	565	747
September	645	520
October	310	558
November	205	317
December	111	261

———— Year One ----- Year Two

4. From the following graph, tell approximately what percent of an average man's life is spent in working.

5. Make a circle graph of a budget for a man who earns $740.00 per month and distributes it as follows:

Insurance	$ 40.00
Food	160.00
Miscellaneous	160.00
Rent and Utilities	176.00
Savings	86.00
Clothes	48.00
Car payment	50.00
Charity	20.00

6.   From the following graph, determine how many heat units are used in getting the substance to a temperature of 105°F.

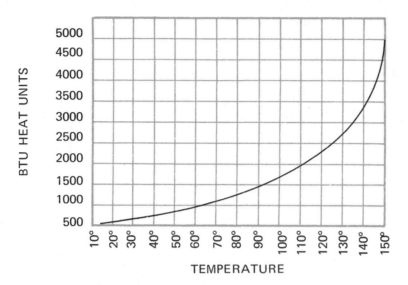

The following graph shows how the average mechanic's salary fluctuates for one particular year.

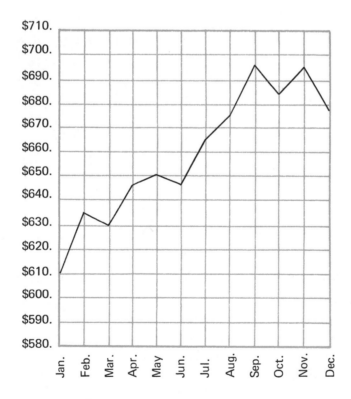

7.   a.   How much did the average mechanic earn in May?   _____

     b.   How much did he earn in July?   _____

8. a. What is the least amount the average mechanic made during the year? _____

    b. What is the largest amount he earned for the year? _____

The following graphs show by comparison how much more efficiently an automobile engine will run when equipped with a high-compression head. Study the following graphs and answer the questions.

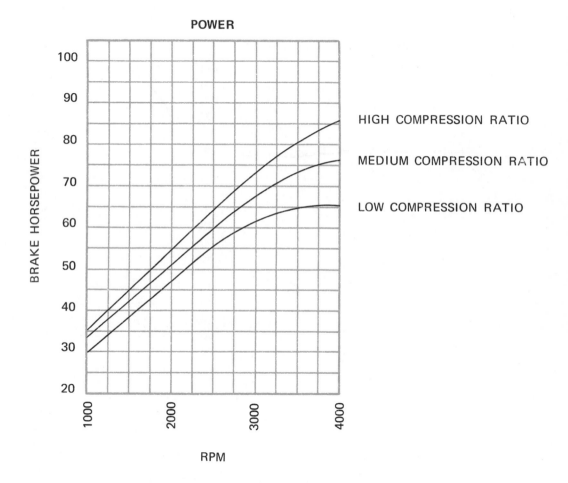

POWER

9. What brake horsepower was developed by the engine having a low-compression ratio when turning over at 3,500 r.p.m.? _____

10. What is the actual difference in generated brake horsepower between two engines at 2,500 r.p.m., one of which is equipped with a low-compression head and the other with a high-compression head? _____

11. How many r.p.m. would a medium-compression head motor be making in order to generate 60 m.p.h.? _____

LOW-COMPRESSION RATIO

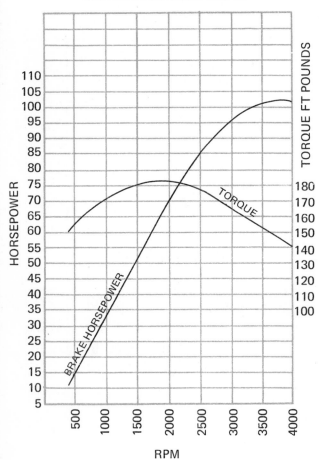

HIGH-COMPRESSION RATIO

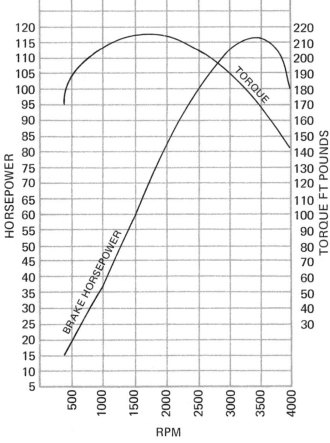

12. At approximately what r.p.m. of a low-compression ratio is maximum torque attained?   _____

13. At approximately what r.p.m. of a high-compression ratio is maximum horsepower attained?   _____

14. At approximately what r.p.m. of a low-compression ratio is maximum horsepower attained?   _____

15. At approximately what r.p.m. of a high-compression ratio is maximum torque attained?   _____

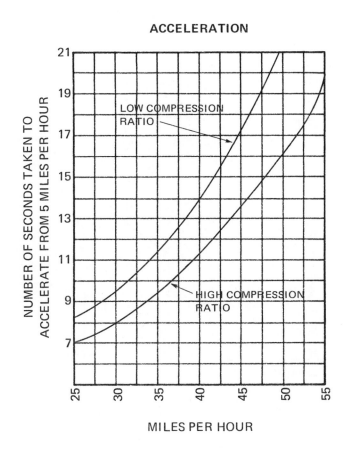

ACCELERATION

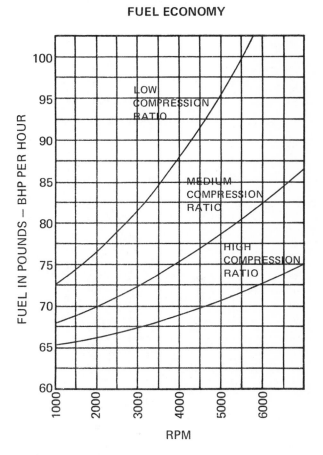

FUEL ECONOMY

Use Acceleration Graph to answer the following question:

16. What is the greatest speed that can be attained in 17 seconds with a car having a high-compression head, starting at 5 miles per hour?   _____

Use Fuel Economy Graph to answer the following questions:

17. a. What type of compression ratio does the car have which consumes the most fuel at 4,000 r.p.m.?   _____

    b. How many pounds of fuel does the car in (a) use?   _____

18. At 75 pounds of fuel per BHP (brake horsepower) per hour, how fast does an automobile engine having a medium-compression ratio rotate in r.p.m.?   _____

19. What is the difference in fuel consumption at 2,750 r.p.m. between a car having a low-compression head, and one having a high-compression head?   _____

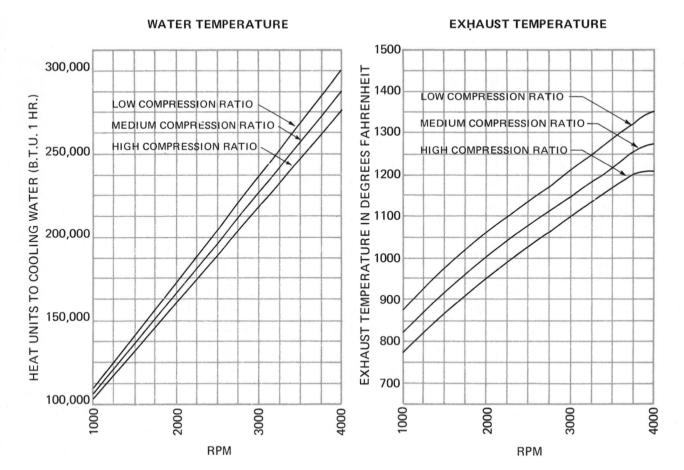

WATER TEMPERATURE

EXHAUST TEMPERATURE

Use Water Temperature Graph to answer the following questions:

20. How many heat units per hour is a high-compression motor at 2,750 r.p.m. returning to the cooling water?   _____

21. How fast is a medium-compression ratio motor rotating when it returns 250,000 heat units per hour to the cooling water?   _____

22. What is the difference at 3,250 r.p.m. between the amounts of heat returned to the cooling water by cars having a low-compression ratio and cars having a high-compression ratio?   _____

Use Exhaust Temperature Graph to answer the following questions:

23. What is the exhaust temperature at 2,250 r.p.m. of the engine having a medium-compression ratio?   _____

24. At 1,150°F. exhaust temperature, how fast is an engine having a low-compression ratio rotating?   _____

25. At 3,000 r.p.m., what is the actual difference in exhaust temperatures between a high-compression and a low-compression ratio car?   _____

Since gasoline will ignite only when mixed in certain proportions with air, it is the function of the carburetor of an automobile engine to mix air with gasoline in the proper proportions for combustion. The ratio of pounds of air admitted to the engine, to the pounds of gasoline to be mixed with it, is known as Air-Fuel Ratio.

With the usual gasoline, a mixture of fifteen pounds of air with one pound of gasoline insures complete combustion. This ideal Air-Fuel Ratio of 15 to 1 is not desired, however, in general practice even though it is most economical in gasoline consumption because the gasoline engine does not develop maximum power at this ratio. The graph indicates that maximum power is obtained in the usual automotive engine with an Air-Fuel Ratio of 12.5 to 13.5 to 1. Since no great loss of power results when the mixture is overrich, there is a tendency to set carbureters on the rich side — and the owner pays for the wasted gas.

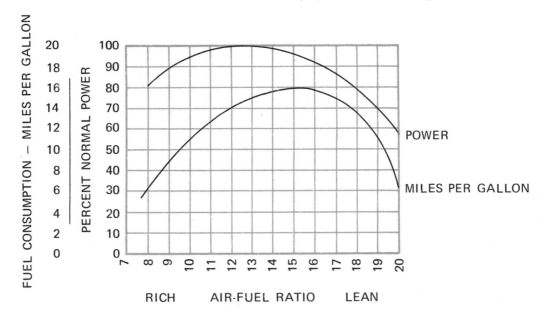

Use the above graph to answer the following questions:

26. At what air-fuel ratio is the best number of miles per gallon of gasoline attained?   _____

27. If too much air is present in the mixture being used, what happens to the number of miles per gallon of gasoline?   _____

28. Does it make much difference in power whether 10 to 1 or 15 to 1 air-fuel ratio is used?   _____

29. What air-fuel ratio gives maximum power?   _____

30. Is the air-fuel ratio which gives the maximum power also the air-fuel ratio which gives the largest number of miles per gallon of gasoline used?   _____

The following data was obtained from an actual test of a motor with its crankshaft speed held constant at 300 r.p.m. while the spark settings were varied.

Total Spark Advance (in degrees)	Brake Horsepower	Exhaust Valve Temperature (in degrees)
10	58.5	1350
20	77.0	1280
30	84.0	1255
40	86.5	1255
50	84.0	1300

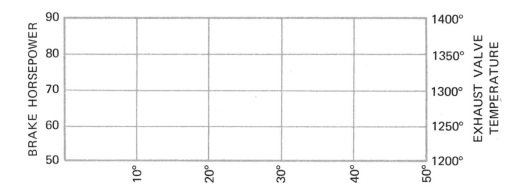

31. Use the chart and the form shown above to make a graph with two curves showing how changes in spark setting affect the brake horsepower and exhaust valve temperature.

32. What spark setting gives the greatest brake horsepower?   _____

33. What is the effect on the horsepower when the spark is advanced a great deal?   _____

34. What is the effect on the exhaust valve temperature when the spark is advanced a great deal?   _____

35. What effect on brake horsepower does a small spark advance have?   _____

36. What effect on the exhaust valve temperature does a small spark advance have?   _____

A flow test may be necessary to determine whether a radiator is clogged. It is determined by the quantity of water that will flow through a radiator (by gravity) in a given time. Certain standards are determined by the manufacturer, and any less water flow indicates clogging. The following is considered typical for certain year-model cars listed:

Buick — 27 gallons per minute

Chevrolet — 19 1/2 gallons per minute

Ford — 42 1/2 gallons per minute

Plymouth — 17 1/2 gallons per minute

37. Plot seconds against gallons of flow in these four graphs from the information given above.

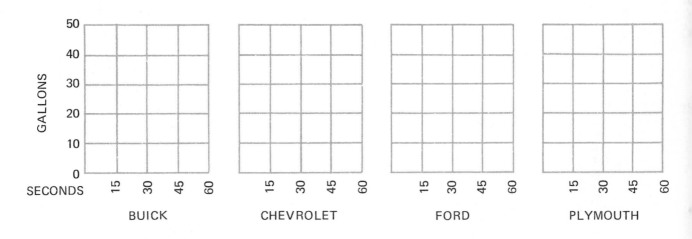

38. In a radiator test on a Buick, a container is placed under the bottom radiator outlet for 10 seconds and 4 gallons of water are collected. Show figures to prove that this radiator test did or did not indicate clogging. _____

39. A Chevrolet is given the radiator test and 26 quarts of water are collected in 20 seconds. Does this test indicate clogging? _____

40. How many quarts should a container hold to be used for a Plymouth radiator test if water is going to be collected for a 30-second test? _____

41. A Ford is to be given the radiator test. If a 5-gallon can is the largest container available, how many seconds may the test be run, assuming the radiator is not clogged? _____

CALCULATING CHART

For Increasing the Protection of "Prestone" Brand Antifreeze Solution

DESIRED FREEZING PROTECTION

+15 +10 +5 0 -5 -10 -15 -20 -25 -30 -35 -40 -45

HOW TO USE THE CHART

1. With a "Prestone" brand ethylene glycol antifreeze tester find out how much freezing protection the solution gives at present.

2. Lay the edge of a ruler from the mark on the left-hand scale representing the present protection, to the mark on the right-hand scale corresponding to the freezing protection desired.

3. Read the first letter above or crossed by the ruler on the lettered scale in the middle of the chart.

4. Turn to the table of Cooling System Capacities and in the column corresponding to the capacity of the car, read the number found on the same lines as the first letter appearing above the ruler.

5. This number represents the quarts of solution to be drawn off from a full cooling system and replaced with undiluted "Prestone" brand antifreeze. This chart reads correctly for "Prestone" brand antifreeze only.

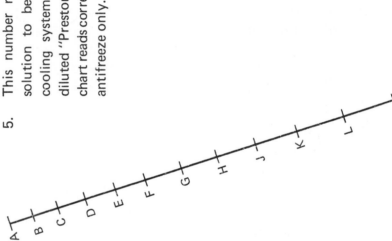

A B C D E F G H J K L

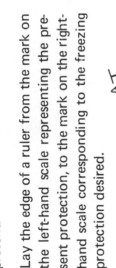
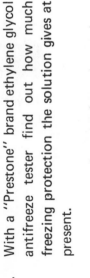

PRESENT FREEZING PROTECTION

-20 -15 -10 -5 0 +5 +10 +15 +20 +25 +30 +32

List of cooling system capacities and quarts of "Prestone" brand antifreeze required. This list is to be used in connection with the Calculating Chart.

Quarts to Replace	Cooling System Capacity					
	2 gal.	3 gal.	4 gal.	5 gal.	6 gal.	7 gal.
A		1	1	1	1	1
B	1	1	2	2	2	3
C	1	2	2	3	4	4
D	2	2	3	4	5	6
E	2	3	4	5	6	7
F	2	4	5	6	7	8
G	3	4	6	7	8	10
H	3	5	6	8	10	11
J	4	5	7	9	11	13
K	4	6	8	10	12	14
L	4	7	9	11	13	15

In the following problems determine the number of quarts of "Prestone" brand antifreeze which are required depending on the conditions as stated in each problem.

Problem	Capacity of System	Present Protection	Desired Protection	Quarts of "Prestone" Antifreeze Required
42.	2 gal.	+20	−20	
43.	3 gal.	+32	−20	
44.	4 gal.	+10	−10	
45.	5 gal.	+20	−10	
46.	6 gal.	+15	−15	
47.	7 gal.	+10	−20	

Unit 40   REPAIR ORDERS, SHOP TICKETS

BASIC PRINCIPLES OF PERCENTAGE AND MONEY CALCULATIONS

- Review units 25, 26, and 29 in *Basic Mathematics Simplified* for the principles of percentage and money calculation as applied to invoices and work orders.

- Apply the principles of percentage and money calculations to the automotive field by solving the Review Problems which follow.

REVIEW PROBLEMS

Invoices: Many times a mechanic is asked (or required) by his employer to fill out shop tickets and/or invoices for the customer.

If the mechanic makes a mistake in favor of the customer (charges too little), he is in trouble with the "boss." After all — he is in business for profit. On the other hand, a mistake in favor of the "boss" is just as serious. Though the mistake may be unintentional, the customer may not think so. Sometimes, if not handled properly, such a mistake may cost the shop a good customer.

The following shop tickets and invoices provide practice that may be helpful. Complete the shop tickets and solve the problems with each.

PROBLEM 1

A major tuneup on an 8-cylinder automobile requires the following parts:

1 set	Spark plugs	@ $1.35 each
1 each	Point set	@ $2.15 each
1 each	Condenser	@ $1.20 each
1 each	Rotor	@ $1.65 each
1 each	Carburetor kit	@ $4.15 each

Flat rate labor for the tuneup is $8.00. Flat rate labor for rebuilding the carburetor is $9.00. Include 3% sales tax in the total charge.

1. The mechanic receives 50% of the labor charge for his salary. _____ What is his pay for this job?

2. If the job requires 3.2 hours to complete, what does the mechanic _____ average per hour?

3. If spark plugs cost $.70 each and the other material costs 40% off _____ list, what profit does the garage owner make on the parts?

PROBLEM 1 — WORK ORDER

MID TOWN GARAGE
212 NORTHERN BLVD.
BROWNVILLE, NEW YORK 13000
TELEPHONE 853-4008

NAME

ADDRESS

CITY

| DATE | CUST. ORDER NO. | WHEN PROMISED | PHONE |

YEAR & MAKE OF CAR TYPE OR MODEL — SERIAL NO.

MOTOR NO.

LICENSE NO. — MILEAGE — WRITTEN BY

DESCRIPTION OF WORK — AMOUNT

GAS, OIL & GREASE

CHECK BELOW
LUBRICATE — LABOR ONLY
GALS. GAS — CHANGE ENGINE OIL — PARTS
QTS. OIL — TRANSMISSION — ACCESSORIES
LBS. GREASE — DIFFERENTIAL — GAS, OIL & GREASE
WASH — MISC. MERCHANDISE
POLISH — SUBLET REPAIRS
TOTAL GAS, OIL & GREASE ► — TOTAL SERVICE ► — TAX

AUTHORIZED BY — TOTAL ►

| AMT. | PART NO. | NAME OF PART | SALE AMT. |

SEE BACK FOR ADDITIONAL PARTS — TOTAL PARTS ►

ACCESSORIES — TIRES AND TUBES

TOTAL ACCESSORIES ►

ESTIMATES ARE FOR LABOR ONLY, MATERIAL ADDITIONAL

PRINTED BY GRAYARC CO., INC., BROOKLYN, N. Y. 11232

I HEREBY AUTHORIZE THE ABOVE REPAIR WORK TO BE DONE ALONG WITH NECESSARY MATERIALS. YOU AND YOUR EMPLOYEES MAY OPERATE ABOVE VEHICLE FOR PURPOSES OF TESTING, INSPECTION OR DELIVERY AT MY RISK. AN EXPRESS MECHANIC'S LIEN IS ACKNOWLEDGED ON ABOVE VEHICLE TO SECURE THE AMOUNT OF REPAIRS THERETO. IT IS UNDERSTOOD THAT THIS COMPANY ASSUMES NO RESPONSIBILITY FOR LOSS OR DAMAGE BY THEFT OR FIRE TO VEHICLES PLACED WITH THEM FOR STORAGE, SALE, REPAIR OR WHILE ROAD TESTING.

PAY THIS AMOUNT

PROBLEM 2

An air-conditioning repair job requires the following parts:

1 each	Seal kit	@ $4.50 each
3 pounds	Refrigerant	@ $1.75 per pound
2 ounces	Oil	@ $ .30 per ounce
42 inches	13/32-inch hose	@ $1.60 per foot
2 each	Hose clamps	@ $ .35 each

Labor charge at $7.00 per hour is as follows:

Seal compressor	1.6 hours
Add Oil	.2 hours
Replace Hose and Clamps	.5 hours
Charge with Refrigerant	1.1 hours

Include 4% sales tax in the total charges.

1. The mechanic is guaranteed $100.00 per week for 40 hours work. What is his hourly guarantee?   _____

2. His commission is 50% of this labor charge. What does he average per hour for this job?   _____

3. All parts used on this job carry a 45% discount off list price. What profit did the owner of the garage make on this job for parts and labor combined?   _____

PROBLEM 2 — WORK ORDER

MID TOWN GARAGE
212 NORTHERN BLVD.
BROWNVILLE, NEW YORK 13000
TELEPHONE 853-4008

NAME

ADDRESS

CITY

DATE	CUST. ORDER NO.	WHEN PROMISED	PHONE

YEAR & MAKE OF CAR-TYPE OR MODEL		SERIAL NO.
		MOTOR NO.

LICENSE NO.	MILEAGE	WRITTEN BY

DESCRIPTION OF WORK — AMOUNT

GAS, OIL & GREASE

	CHECK BELOW	
GALS. GAS	LUBRICATE	
QTS. OIL	CHANGE ENGINE OIL	
LBS. GREASE	TRANSMISSION	
	DIFFERENTIAL	
	WASH	
	POLISH	
TOTAL GAS, OIL & GREASE ►	TOTAL SERVICE ►	

AUTHORIZED BY

PART NO.	NAME OF PART	SALE AMT.

AMT.

SEE BACK FOR ADDITIONAL PARTS   TOTAL PARTS ►

ACCESSORIES — TIRES AND TUBES

TOTAL ACCESSORIES ►

LABOR ONLY

PARTS

ACCESSORIES

GAS, OIL & GREASE

MISC. MERCHANDISE

SUBLET REPAIRS

TAX

TOTAL ►

PAY THIS AMOUNT ◄

ESTIMATES ARE FOR LABOR ONLY, MATERIAL ADDITIONAL

I HEREBY AUTHORIZE THE ABOVE REPAIR WORK TO BE DONE ALONG WITH NECESSARY MATERIALS. YOU AND YOUR EMPLOYEES MAY OPERATE ABOVE VEHICLE FOR PURPOSES OF TESTING, INSPECTION OR DELIVERY AT MY RISK. AN EXPRESS MECHANIC'S LIEN IS ACKNOWLEDGED ON ABOVE VEHICLE TO SECURE THE AMOUNT OF REPAIRS THERETO. IT IS UNDERSTOOD THAT THIS COMPANY ASSUMES NO RESPONSIBILITY FOR LOSS OR DAMAGE BY THEFT OR FIRE TO VEHICLES PLACED WITH THEM FOR STORAGE, SALE, REPAIR OR WHILE ROAD TESTING.

PRINTED BY GRAYARC CO., INC., BROOKLYN, N. Y. 11232

PROBLEM 3

While a cooling system is being cleaned, it is learned that the radiator is clogged and must be cleaned. The car owner asks that all hoses, thermostat, and pressure cap be replaced. The job requires the following parts:

30 inches	5/8-inch hose	@ $ .36 per foot
24 inches	3/4-inch hose	@ $ .45 per foot
2 each	5/8-inch hose clamps	@ $ .26 each
2 each	3/4-inch hose clamps	@ $ .28 each
1 each	Thermostat	@ $2.65 each
1 each	Pressure cap	@ $1.95 each
1 each	Upper hose	@ $3.20 each
1 each	Lower hose	@ $2.95 each
4 each	Hose clamps	@ $ .39 each
1 pint	Rust inhibitor	@ $1.25 per pint

Labor charges are as follows:

Remove, clean, and replace radiator . . .	$12.50
Reverse flush block	$ 3.50
Replace heater hoses	$ 2.50
Replace thermostat and cap.	N/C

Include 4% sales tax in the total charges.

1. The total job takes 3 hours. The mechanic receives 60% of his labor charges. What is he paid for the job?   _____

2. What is the mechanic's average hourly earnings?   _____

3. The garage owner receives 40% discount for parts. What does he pay for the parts for this job?   _____

MIDTOWN GARAGE

212 NORTHERN BLVD.
BROWNVILLE, NEW YORK 13000
TELEPHONE 853-4008

NAME

ADDRESS

CITY   PHONE

MAKE   MODEL   YEAR   SER. NO.   LICENSE NO.

MTR. NO.

OPER. NO.

RECEIVED A.M. P.M.   DATE

PROMISED A.M. P.M.   CUSTOMER ORDER NO.

TERMS   ORDER WRITTEN BY

SPEEDOMETER

LABOR CHARGE

REPAIR ORDER INSTRUCTIONS

LUBRICATE   CHANGE OIL   FLUSH TRANS.   FLUSH DIFF.   WASH   POLISH

I hereby authorize the above repair work to be done along with the necessary material, and hereby grant you and/or your employees permission to operate the car or truck herein described on streets, highways or elsewhere for the purpose of testing and/or inspection. An express mechanic's lien is hereby acknowledged on above car or truck to secure the amount of repairs thereto.

X

NOT RESPONSIBLE FOR LOSS OR DAMAGE TO CARS OR ARTICLES LEFT IN CARS IN CASE OF FIRE, THEFT OR ANY OTHER CAUSE BEYOND OUR CONTROL.

F. S.

GAS OIL AND GREASE

	PRICE
GALS. GAS @	
QTS. OIL @	
LBS. GREASE @	
TOTAL GAS, OIL AND GREASE	

PHONE WHEN READY:

TOTAL LABOR	
TOTAL PARTS	
ACCESSORIES	
GAS, OIL & GREASE	
OUTSIDE REPAIRS	
TAX	
TOTAL AMOUNT	

MATERIAL USED

QUAN.	PART NO.	DESCRIPTION	PRICE

OUTSIDE REPAIRS

BROUGHT FORWARD

TOTAL PARTS

QUAN.	ACCES. NO.	ACCESSORIES	PRICE

TOTAL ACCESSORIES

GRO-1 ®

PROBLEM 4

A car broke down 12 miles from the garage. Towing service is $5.00 for a 3-mile radius and $1.00 per mile thereafter (figuring one-way mileage). Add 5% sales tax.

1. From the time the mechanic leaves the shop, until he returns, he averages 15 miles per hour.   How long is he away from the shop?   _____

2. What does the shop owner average per hour for the call, not considering any cost?   _____

3. The mechanic receives 50% of the shop charges for his salary. What does he earn for the trip?   _____

4. What is the mechanic's average pay per hour for the trip?   _____

5. The shop owner figures his expenses of operating the truck, against his charges, as follows:

Mechanic-driver	50%
Gas and oil	4%
Insurance	4%
Depreciation	5%
Tires and misc.	3%
Shop overhead	10%

What is the shop owner's profit (if any) for the trip?   _____

MIDTOWN GARAGE

212 NORTHERN BLVD.
BROWNVILLE, NEW YORK 13000
TELEPHONE 853-4008

NAME	RECEIVED	DATE
	A.M. / P.M.	
ADDRESS	PROMISED	CUSTOMER ORDER NO.
	A.M. / P.M.	
CITY	PHONE	TERMS	ORDER WRITTEN BY

MAKE	MODEL	YEAR	SER. NO.	LICENSE NO.	SPEEDOMETER
			MTR. NO.		

REPAIR ORDER INSTRUCTIONS

OPER. NO.		LABOR CHARGE
LUBRI-CATE ○	CHANGE OIL ○	FLUSH TRANS. ○	FLUSH DIFF. ○	WASH ○	POLISH ○

OUTSIDE REPAIRS

BROUGHT FORWARD

TOTAL PARTS

ACCESSORIES PRICE

I hereby authorize the above repair work to be done along with the necessary material, and hereby grant you and/or your employees permission to operate the car or truck herein described on streets, highways or elsewhere for the purpose of testing and/or inspection. An express mechanic's lien is hereby acknowledged on above car or truck to secure the amount of repairs thereto.

X

NOT RESPONSIBLE FOR LOSS OR DAMAGE TO CARS OR ARTICLES LEFT IN CARS IN CASE OF FIRE, THEFT OR ANY OTHER CAUSE BEYOND OUR CONTROL.

GAS OIL AND GREASE		PRICE
GALS. GAS @		
QTS. OIL @		
LBS. GREASE @		
TOTAL GAS, OIL AND GREASE		

F. S.

PHONE WHEN READY: ○

TOTAL LABOR	
TOTAL PARTS	
ACCESSORIES	
GAS, OIL & GREASE	
OUTSIDE REPAIRS	
TAX	
TOTAL AMOUNT	

MATERIAL USED

QUAN.	PART NO.	DESCRIPTION	PRICE

TOTAL PARTS

ACCESSORIES

QUAN.	ACCES. NO.	PRICE

TOTAL ACCESSORIES

GRO-1 ®

105

ACHIEVEMENT REVIEW A

1. A family on an automobile trip covered the following distances each day: Monday, 388 miles; Tuesday, 279 miles; Wednesday, 307 miles; Thursday, 213 miles; Friday, 209 miles. What total distance is covered in the five days? _____

2. In a period of one month, Station A sold 28,637 gallons of gasoline, while Station B sold 36,895 gallons. How many more gallons did Station B sell than Station A? _____

3. There are 4 rings per piston in a certain 8-cylinder engine. How many rings are needed for 16 engines of this type? _____

4. Gas Station A sells 16,845 gallons in a 15-day period. What is its average daily sales? _____

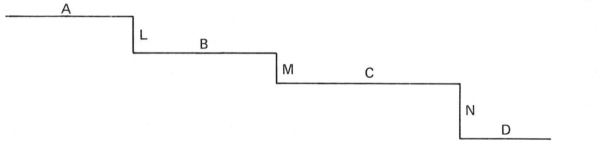

5. Measure and give the total length of A + B + C + D. _____

6. Measure and give the total length of L + M + N. _____

7. Find the outside diameter of the tire. _____

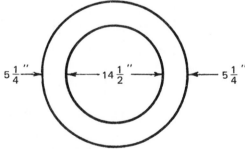

8. What is the length of this block? _____

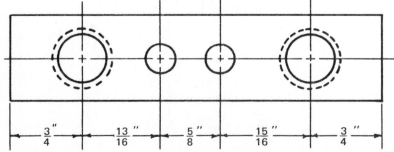

106

9. Find "X", the amount to be cut off. _____

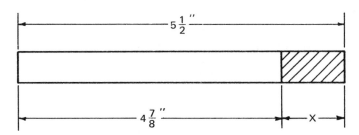

10. Find dimension C of the shaft, if A = 7/8", B = 1 1/4", D = 1 3/16", _____
    and E = 6 1/16".

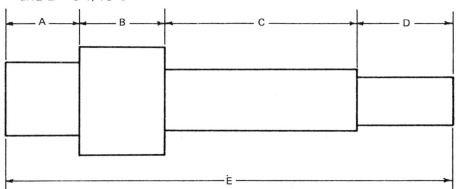

11. A mechanic cuts 7 pieces of copper tubing each 35 3/4 inches long from _____
    a coil. What is the total length used?

12. The number of amperes of electricity through a wire can be found by _____
    dividing the number of volts by the number of ohms resistance. In a
    12-volt circuit, how many amperes of electricity are there through a
    wire which has a resistance of 1 1/2 ohms?

13. What is the drill size 1/32 inch larger than 5/8 inch? _____

14. Five gage blocks are combined to give a certain dimension. What is _____
    this dimension if the blocks measure 2 inches, .350 inch, .140 inch, .104
    inch, and .1007 inch?

15. If .034 inch is cut off a clevis pin 1.125 inches long, what is the length _____
    of the cut pin?

16. A bushing .785 inch long must be cut to .759 inch. How much is it _____
    shortened?

17. If it costs $.075 per mile for fixed costs and $.035 per mile for oper- _____
    ating costs, what is the total cost of running a car 1,237 miles?

18. The cost of 27 ignition tuneup sets is $75.33. What is the cost per set? _____

19. Give the fractional equivalents of the following percentages (%):

    a. 35% _____

    b. 37 1/2% _____

20. A mechanic earning $2.65 per hour receives a 14% increase in pay. What is his new hourly rate?   _____

21. A man works the following times on five different days: 8 hours, 7 hours 45 minutes, 8 hours 15 minutes, 8 hours 10 minutes, and 7 hours 25 minutes. What is his average working time per day?   _____

22. Three pieces of heater hose each 2 feet 7 inches long are cut from a 10-foot length. How much is left?   _____

23. The diameter of a circle equals the circumference divided by π (approx. 3 1/7). If the circumference of a circle is 4 1/8 inches, what is the diameter?   _____

24. 1 circle = 360°. What part of a circle is an arc of 72°?   _____

25. How many degrees are there in angle A?   _____

26. How many minutes are equal to 1.3 hours?   _____

27. Two gears have a speed ratio of 2.8:1. If the larger gear has 56 teeth, how many teeth does the smaller gear have?   _____

28. The amount of taper of a machine tool is the difference in the diameters of the two ends. What is the amount of taper in a tool that has end diameters of 7/8 inch and 1 1/4 inches?   _____

29. If 60 miles per hour = 88 feet per second, express 18 miles per hour in feet per second.   _____

30. Raise the following expressions to the power indicated.

    a. 6^2 _____   b. 12^2 _____   c. 13^2 _____

31. Find $\sqrt{729}$.   _____

32. If area = .7854d^2, find the area when the diameter is 8 inches. (Give answer to the nearest thousandths of an inch.)   _____

33. Use the formula H.P. = $\dfrac{D^2 N}{2.5}$, where D^2 = cylinder bore squared, and N = number of cylinders. Find H.P. (horsepower) of a 6-cylinder engine with a bore of 3.5 inches.   _____

ACHIEVEMENT REVIEW B

1. Orders for 10, 23, 15, and 17 filters are filled from a stock of 137 filters. How many filters are left in stock after filling the orders? _____

2. An automobile was purchased with 13,746 miles on the odometer. The reading is now 32,967 miles. How far has the present owner driven the car? _____

3. An engine turns 650 revolutions per minute. How many revolutions will it turn in 27 minutes? _____

4. There are 3 long rocker-arm springs for each of the two heads of a V8 engine. How many springs are needed for 54 V8 engines? _____

5. Mycar Company sells 14,985 automobiles in a 45-day period. What is the average daily sales of this company? _____

Give the scale readings as indicated. Record each dimension in the space provided.

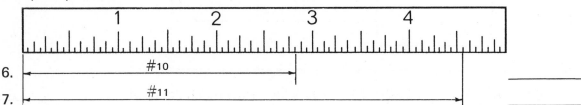

6. _____

7. _____

8. What is the overall length of the shaft? _____

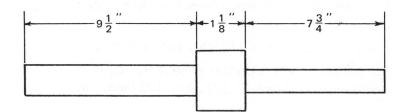

9. What is the length of this block? _____

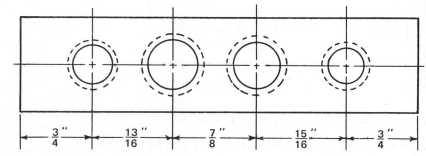

109

10. Find "X", the amount to be cut off.   _____

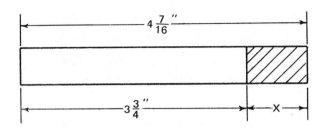

11. Find dimension B of the bushing driver, if A = 7/8", C = 2 3/16", and   _____
    D = 4 1/8".

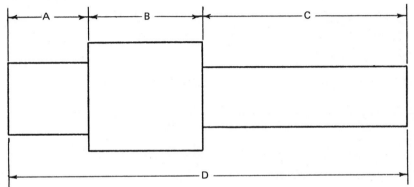

12. A certain type crankshaft weighs 33 1/2 pounds. How much do 12 of   _____
    these crankshafts weigh?

13. If a man drives a car 327 3/4 miles a day, how far does he drive at this   _____
    rate in 5 1/2 days?

14. If 1/3 barrel holds 10 1/2 gallons, how many gallons are there in one   _____
    barrel?

15. How many 7/8-inch pins can be cut from a 14-inch piece of steel rod?   _____

16. Four gage blocks are combined to give a certain dimension. What is   _____
    this dimension if the blocks measure 3 inches, .250 inch, .139 inch, and
    .1004 inch?

17. What is the center-to-center distance X between the holes?   _____

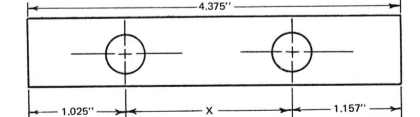

18. If the cost of oil is $1.37 per gallon, what do 55 gallons cost?   _____

19. What is the average mileage per gallon of gasoline, if a car runs 616.4   _____
    miles on 33.5 gallons?

20. The cost of 19 ignition wiring sets is $69.16. What is the cost per set? _____

21. A mechanic received 55% of the total labor on a certain job. If the job took 4 hours and was billed at $7.50 per hour for labor, how much did the mechanic receive? _____

22. A parts salesman receives 7% commission on parts he sells. If he sells $139.00 worth of parts, what is his commission? _____

23. Change 485 inches to yards, feet, and inches. _____

24. Two pieces of copper tubing, one 1 foot 4 inches long and the other 2 feet 7 inches long, are cut from a 10-foot length of tubing. What length remains? _____

25. The diameter of a circle equals the circumference divided by π (approx. 3 1/7). If the circumference of a circle is 8 1/4 inches, what is the diameter? _____

26. 1 circle = 360°. What part of a circle is an arc of 40°? _____

27. How many degrees are in angle A? _____

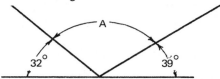

28. How many minutes are equal to .8 hour? _____

29. Two gears have a speed ratio of 3.7:1. If the larger gear has 74 teeth, how many teeth does the smaller gear have? _____

30. Standard taper pins all have a taper of 1/4 inch per foot. What is the difference in diameters between the two ends of a taper pin which is 3 inches long? _____

31. If area = πR^2 for a circle, find the area when the radius is 14 inches. (Use π = 3 1/7.) _____

32. Use the formula H.P. = $\dfrac{D^2 N}{2.5}$, where D^2 = cylinder bore squared, and N = number of cylinders. Find H.P. (horsepower) when the engine is a V8 with a bore of 3.75 inches. _____

Acknowledgments

Publications Director
   Alan N. Knofla

Editor-in-Chief
   Marjorie Bruce

Sponsoring Editor
   Elinor Gunnerson

Consulting Editor
   Robert E. Carlberg,
   Anaheim, California

Revision
   Boyce Dwiggins

Production Director
   Frederick Sharer

Production Specialists
   Gloria Hollister
   Jean Le Morta
   Lee St. Onge

Illustration
   Anthony Canabush
   Michael Kokernak